Solving Equations
A Conceptual Approach

Developed and Published
by

AIMS Education Foundation

This book contains materials developed by the AIMS Education Foundation. **AIMS** (**A**ctivities **I**ntegrating **M**athematics and **S**cience) began in 1981 with a grant from the National Science Foundation. The non-profit AIMS Education Foundation publishes hands-on instructional materials that build conceptual understanding. The foundation also sponsors a national program of professional development through which educators may gain expertise in teaching math and science.

AIMS Education Foundation
P.O. Box 8120, Fresno, CA 93747-8120 • 888.733.2467 • aimsedu.org

ISBN 978-1-932093-44-5

Printed in the United States of America

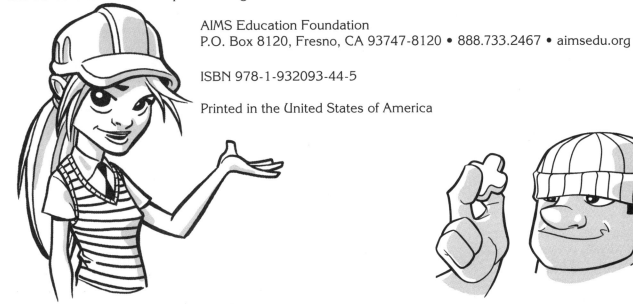

Table of Contents

I Hear and I Forget,

I See and I Remember,

I Do and I Understand.

-Chinese Proverb

Why a Conceptual Approach

What we do

We need to find a way to teach more, better, and faster if we are going to help students meet more rigorous standards. Being pressed for time, math teachers use what appears to be most efficient, direct instruction of procedural practices. To solve equations, we provide the students with a set of rules and steps that we teach them very incrementally. Can you hear the class? "Move the x's to one side and the numbers to the other. Deal with the additions and subtractions first. Use the inverse operation. Next deal with multiplications and divisions." The first lessons involve one-step solutions, then two-steps, then variables on both sides of the equality, finally groupings requiring distribution. By the time students get to this level, they are lost. First, they have no feel for what the variable means. It is just another symbol to be pushed around the page. The procedure has become so complex that some of the original steps seem to contradict the last steps. If the student does manage to keep track of the procedure, it seems meaningless and useless so is quickly forgotten. So, to help their memory we assign a lot of problems, but this only discourages them. When we are done, we have disgruntled students who have a minimal understanding of how to solve equations and even less reason for doing so. Is direct instruction of procedural practices the best way to learn math?

What we should do

Research shows that students learn math best when they develop conceptual understanding first and then formalize it into abstract procedures. Several studies (Kieran (1984), Pesek and Kirshner (2000)) compared students that received only active hands-on experience to those who first received formal instruction in the procedure that was followed with the active hands-on learning. While receiving less then half the instructional time, those having only hands-on, conceptually-based instruction scored as well as those who received procedural instruction before their hands-on experience. Not only did they learn as well in a shorter time, but those students having only the conceptual experience also retained it longer and were able to apply their knowledge in more novel situations. The research demonstrates that we can teach more, better, and faster if we develop conceptual understanding initially to be followed with more abstract procedures when students can recognize the meaning of and reason for their actions.

How we can do it

The investigations in this book are based on this conceptual-development model. Activity begins with hands-on experience. Dealing with objects or contexts, students physically work through solutions. A record is made of the actions. As students work though a series of situations, they begin to make sense of the symbolic record and gain a memory of physically working out the solutions. With experience, students begin to see the related patterns of their repetitive solutions and the symbolic records. As students are asked to summarize what they have done, they clarify the procedure needed to solve the problems and understand why they are following each step. This sequence of instruction provides a lasting understanding of the procedure.

It's good for the kids

The research shows the sequence of developing procedural learning from conceptual understanding allows us to teach more, better, and faster. But an added bonus, or perhaps the reason for the increased learning, is that students like to learn this way. The physical nature of the investigations encourages students to be engaged. They like "playing" with the stuff. Students see the learning as purposeful because the investigations are set in contexts that help students recognize the usefulness of what they are learning. They figure things out not to get an answer for a teacher but to act out being a pirate, banker, or clerk. We all recognize that "aha" moment as the sign of true learning. You do not hear, "I get it!" when someone has mastered a sequence of how to solve a problem, but when they understand how something works. Students like getting the "aha" experience, and they get that understanding at a conceptual level. You don't forget what you learned when you have an "aha" experience. With hands-on, conceptual learning, students will have the "aha" experiences that will provide a memory of how to work through those abstract problems. As they play at math to develop a conceptual understanding, they are building the foundation of a lasting understanding.

v

The Concepts

The Prerequisites

Before students start to solve equations, they must become familiar with the meaning of symbolic expressions. The first two activities in the book, *What's in the Bank?* and *Widgets Inc.*, help develop foundational understanding for solving equations and help students avoid developing common misconceptions.

The most fundamental aspect of algebra is the variable. The concept of variable has multiple meanings depending on its use; this causes difficulty for students. In a function, the variable is used as one of the values in a relationship. In this case, the value can vary, so the meaning of variable matches the use of the word. In other situations, the variable does not vary, but represents a constant. In the typical physics formula $f = ma$, a represents the acceleration of gravity, which is a constant 32 ft/sec^2 on Earth. When solving equations with only one variable, the variable does not vary, but is a constant unknown. It takes a good deal of experience with variables until students are able to differentiate between the different the uses or meanings of a variable. Without an understanding of what a variable is, students often develop misconceptions that cause them difficulty as they begin to solve equations. Hands-on conceptual lessons help students avoid these misconceptions by allowing them to construct a clear meaning of the variable for themselves.

Combining like terms is often misunderstood because the variable has no meaning and students do what makes sense from past experience. Consider the expression $x^2 + 3x + 4 + 2x$. The response from students is varied. If a student simplifies the expression to $10x$, he or she has simply added the values of all the terms. Another might give $7x + 4$ as the simplification, knowing that numbers are different from variables, but not recognizing that x^2 is not the same as $3x$ or $2x$. The activity *What's in the Bank?* uses different letters to represent different variables (drawers *(d)* or stacks*(s)*) so students understand that only the same variables can be combined. *Widgets Inc.* uses algebra tiles as pallets (p^2), packs (p), and units. The distinct form of each object is related to its symbolic representation. Students do not even think of combining flat square pallets with the stick-like packs to get a single count of objects. As students become comfortable with the symbols, they differentiate between p^2 and p. Through this process, students have acquired a conceptual reason for not combining the symbols and have avoided a misconception that develops when symbols alone are used.

To solve more complex equations, students need to develop an understanding of distribution. In *What's in the Bank?* and *Widgets Inc.*, multiple equal sets are used to introduce distribution. In *What's in the Bank?*, problems take the form of describing the contents of a bank. For example, students are asked to determine the amount of money in a bank with three vaults each containing two drawers $(2d)$, five stacks $(5s)$, and eight dollars (8). The record matches the context, and with a visual concept of the situation, students are able to complete the equality $(3(2d + 5s + 8) = 6d + 15s + 24)$. In *Widgets Inc.*, the problems are framed in the context of determining what is left on a loading dock when, for example, three loads of two pallets $(2p^2)$, five packs $(5p)$, and 8 units are delivered. By manipulating the materials, students combine the pallets, packs, and units to get a total count. As they record the results, they gain a conceptual understanding that is related to the symbolic record $(3(2p^2 + 5p + 8) = 6p^2 + 15p + 24)$.

Solving Equations—Two Concepts

Solving equations requires the understanding of the concepts of inverse operations and equality. Students who have worked with numbers understand these concepts, but need to become comfortable using them with variables.

The activity *Jumping to Solutions* has a student take several jumps along a tape measure beginning from a point other than zero. The class is then asked to determine the length of one of the student's jumps. If the student started at 140 centimeters and took four jumps to end at 320 centimeters, many students will suggest subtracting the two distances to determine how far the student jumped (320 – 140 = 180). Since the student went 180 centimeters in four jumps, the class will suggest dividing the distance jumped by four (180 ÷ 4 = 45) to get a jump length of 45 centimeters. Students who follow this logic have the understanding needed to solve equations, but have not grown accustomed to using variables. Asking students to describe the actions with words prepares them to translate the verbal description into algebraic terms. Students say, "The jumper started at 140 and took four jumps to end up at 320." This description is translated into the equation $140 + 4J = 320$ where J equals the length of a jump. As students transform this equation with the steps they used to solve the problem, they begin to recognize the steps required to solve the equation. First, they subtract the 140 centimeters at the beginning of the tape. This means the four jumps totaled 180 centimeters.

$$
\begin{aligned}
140 + 4J &= 320 \\
-140 \qquad &\; -140 \\
\hline
4J &= 180
\end{aligned}
$$

Next, they split up the 180 centimeters into four equal pieces to see how long one jump was.

$$\frac{4J}{4} = \frac{180}{4}$$

$$J = 45$$

As students match what they intuitively know how to do with numbers to the algebraic representations, they become comfortable with the manipulation of the symbols. As students approach more contexts from the numeric and conceptual angle, they will develop habits of understanding that naturally develop meaningful manipulations of the algebraic symbols.

Inverse Operations—Backtracking Problems

The *Tracking Treasure* and *Extraordinary Solution Prediction* series of investigations develop the concept of inverse operations. In *Tracking Treasure*, students are given a clue that describes how a pirate moved from a chest of buried treasure to where the clue was hidden. If x marks the spot where the treasure is hidden, a clue might be $2x - 5 = 3$. Starting at the third position, the treasure hunter would work backward in the inverse order the pirate did things. The last thing the pirate did was to take five steps backward, so the inverse would be to take five steps forward, landing the treasure hunter in the eighth position. The first thing the pirate did was to double his position. Inversely, the treasure hunter would divide his position by two, taking him to the fourth position, where the treasure is buried. To find the treasure, the hunter backtracks through the events in the inverse order the pirate did them.

In the *E.S.P.—Extraordinary Solution Prediction* series, a "magician" appears to read a person's mind and know what number a person started with after the number has been changed by a series of operations. The secret to the trick is that the magician has translated the operations to algebra and simply backtracks from the ending number by doing the inverse of each operation to report the starting number. Reducing a long series of instructions to a simple equation speeds up the magic. A typical set of simplified instructions might be $2n + 5$. When 19 is volunteered as an ending number, the magician quickly subtracts five and divides by two to get the starting number of seven. Backtracking solves the equation by using inverse operations to undo what was done.

Equality—Not Obvious

Students understand that an equals sign states that there is equal value on both sides. But few students have thought that if you add, subtract, multiply, or divide one side, doing the same to the other side will maintain the equality. Although it seems self-evident, it is not obvious to students. *Equality in the Balance* has students move pennies and packets filled with unknown numbers of pennies on a balance to act out solutions to equations. One situation might have students balance three packets and five pennies on one side of the balance with 26 pennies on the other side. Students can write out the description as an equation: $3p + 5 = 26$. To maintain the equilibrium, students can remove five pennies from both sides. This is recorded.

$$3p + 5 = 26$$
$$\underline{ -5 \quad -5}$$
$$3p = 21$$

To determine the pennyweight of each packet, what is in each pan is split into three groups so each packet balances seven pennies. This is recorded.

$$\frac{3p}{3} = \frac{21}{3}$$
$$p = 7$$

As students act out a number of equation solutions, they internalize the concept of maintaining equality by operating on both sides of an equation equally. Making a symbolic record of what is done builds their confidence until they can solve equations without the balance.

Combining the Concepts

The two concepts of equality and inverse operations are used to solve equations. Each of the prior activities emphasizes one of these concepts. *What's in a Case?* is a set of investigations in which students reinforce both concepts to determine how many items are in a case that is shipped to them without opening the box. It, like all the other activities, introduces students to simple one-step solutions and has a number of levels that build to complex multi-step solutions. This allows the teacher to determine what level is most appropriate for the students.

Advanced Topics

The last four investigations provide activities that develop conceptual understanding of more advanced topics where the process of solving equations is used. *Pogo Stick Paths* introduces the concept of solving multiple equations at the same time. Dealing with systems of equations or solving simultaneous equations is a topic that is part of a formal study of algebra and is becoming a more typical topic for introduction in middle school. *Pogo Stick Paths* extends the ideas introduced in *Jumping to Solutions* and provides a very visual way to think about solutions. (More investigations developing the concepts of systems of equations can be found in the AIMS publication *Looking at Lines*.)

An area of algebra that is difficult for students is mixture problems or weighted averages. *Leveled Loads* extends the application of a balance to develop the concept of mixtures with hands-on experience. *Shades of Gray* encourages students to approach these problems from a visual model. *Watered Down Temperatures* uses technology (spreadsheet) to simulate mixing fluids of different temperatures. Students record numeric results and generalize patterns that are solved algebraically. This series provides a smooth transition to help students develop a conceptual understanding while helping them to move to an abstract but meaningful solution.

Understanding Over Time

Understanding the concept of solving for an unknown is best developed over a period of several years. One should not anticipate completing all the investigations in this book during one school year. Ideally, teachers at one school site would discuss the standards for each grade level and determine the appropriate investigations for each. A school might choose to have the sixth grade students complete *What's in the Bank? Tracking Treasure Part One, Backtracking Extraordinary Solution Predictions,* and the initial section of *What's in a Case?*. The seventh grade classes might work on *Widgets Inc., Jumping to Solutions, Manipulating ESP,* do the initial parts of *Equality in the Balance,* and complete the last half of *What's in a Case?* The eighth grade students could work on *ESP: Extraordinary Solution Predictions,* the remaining part of *Equality in the Balance, Tracking Treasure Part Two,* and *Pogo Stick Paths.* The investigations, *Leveled Loads, Shades of Gray,* and *Watered Down Temperatures* could be used in a formal algebra class.

Using the hands-on investigations in this book will allow your students to develop an understanding of how and why they need to do things to solve for an unknown. This conceptual understanding is the foundation that will provide success in the process of solving for unknowns required in all of algebra.

Works Cited

Kieran, C. (1984). A comparison between novice and more-expert algebra students on tasks dealing with the equivalence of equations. In J. M. Moser (Ed.), *Proceedings of the sixth annual meeting of the North American chapter of the International Group for the Psychology of Mathematics Education* (pp. 83-91). Madison, WI: University of Wisconsin.

Pesek, D., & Kirshner, D. (2000). Interference of instrumental instruction in subsequent relational learning. *Journal for Research in Mathematics Education, 31,* 524-540.

DVD Resources

Three types of resources are included on the accompanying DVD for you to use with the investigations in this book.

1 The first resource is a series of videos that inform the teacher in the use of the investigations. The rationale for the development of the activities is presented. The big ideas and suggestions of how to make the investigation most successful are discussed. A sample of the activity being used in the classroom is shown. The five videos are:

Introduction: The Conceptual Approach
Become acquainted with the research and reasons for using a conceptual approach. Discusses how using a conceptual approach allows students to learn more, better, and faster.

Part One: Contexts for Thinking
See how contexts and manipulatives provide an environment for conceptual development. Looks at the ideas of combining like terms and distribution with the activities *What's in the Bank?* and *Widgets, Inc.*

Part Two: Multiple Representations
Learn how multiple representations allow students to relate conceptual understanding to abstract reasoning. Relates the process of solving equations to arithmetic by looking at the activity *Jumping to Solutions.*

Part Three: Equalities
Recognize the key idea of the concept of equalities in solving equations and learn how to develop this concept using the activities *Equality in the Balance* and *What's in a Case?*

Part Four: Inverse Operations
Recognize the key idea of inverse operations as a process of solving equations. Shows how students backtrack solutions in *ESP: Extraordinary Solution Prediction* and the *Tracking Treasure* activities.

2 The second resource is a set of animations of the characters on the student pages that set up the contextual activities. These animations help the students understand the context of the activity and are designed to engage the students by helping them recognize the possible application of what they are learning in the investigation. The following activities have an animation:

Animation	Activities
Bank Intro	*What's in the Bank?*
Widgets Intro	*Widgets Inc.*
ESP Intro	*Backtracking ESP*
	Manipulating ESP
	ESP: Extraordinary Solution Prediction
Tracks1 Intro	*Tracking Treasure: Part One*
Tracks2 Intro	*Tracking Treasure: Part Two*
Case Intro	*What's in a Case?*

3 The last resource is all of the printable pages from this book in PDF format. Additionally, the video resources can be accessed at our website. Go to www.aimsedu.org/media/books/. Choose the book *Solving Equations* and select the resource desired.

WHAT'S IN THE BANK?

Topic
Mathematical properties

Key Question
How can you use symbols to keep track of what's in the bank?

Learning Goals
Students will:
- translate the contents of a bank into algebraic expressions,
- symbolically combine the contents of several banks to conceptualize combining of like terms, and
- develop an understanding of the distributive property by considering the contents of like vaults in a bank.

Guiding Documents
Project 2061 Benchmark
- *An equation containing a variable may be true for just one value of the variable.*

NCTM Standards 2000*
- *Develop an initial conceptual understanding of different uses of variables*
- *Use symbolic algebra to represent situations and to solve problems, especially those that involve linear relationships*
- *Recognize and generate equivalent forms for simple algebraic expressions and solve linear equations*

Math
Number
    distributive property
Algebra
    variables
    simplifying expressions

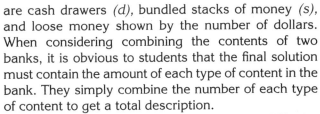

Integrated Processes
Observing
Comparing and contrasting
Generalizing

Materials
Bank Intro animation (see *Management 2*)
Student pages

Background Information
Students initially have difficulty simplifying algebraic expressions because they do not have a clear understanding of the meaning of different variables. They often combine x and x^2 because the exponent does not have meaning to them outside of number. The bank context provides very distinguishable variables. There

are cash drawers (d), bundled stacks of money (s), and loose money shown by the number of dollars. When considering combining the contents of two banks, it is obvious to students that the final solution must contain the amount of each type of content in the bank. They simply combine the number of each type of content to get a total description.

The distributive property often causes difficulty in simplifying. The familiar bank context provides a meaningful application of distribution. If banks have multiple vaults with identical contents, one determines the bank's total content by multiplying what is in each vault by the number of vaults. The student multiplies the number of drawers, the number of stacks, and the amount of loose money by the number of vaults. The symbolic representation of this property becomes meaningful when considering the bank context.

Management
1. The teacher instruction video *Part One: Contexts for Thinking* is on the accompanying DVD. It is also available at the following URL: www.aimsedu. org/media/books/. It provides the rationale and suggestions for using this activity successfully in your classroom.
2. The animation *Bank Intro* is on the accompanying DVD and at the URL listed above. Make preparations in your classroom so students can view the animation. If viewing through a computer, a projector enhances the experience.
3. This investigation develops two concepts that are best treated as separate lessons. *Part One* develops the concepts of combining terms with like variables and establishes the context of bank problems. *Part Two* develops a meaningful context for the distributive property. Both parts have one student page to guide exploration and development of understanding and a second page to reinforce and practice the concepts.
4. The context is represented with pictures, and many students can solve the problems by simply using the picture. To help students move from the intuitive understanding to understanding the concepts in symbolic form, make sure they demonstrate their thinking symbolically too.

Procedure
Part One
1. If available, show the students the *Bank Intro* animation.
2. Explain the context to the students making sure they

understand the three distinct types of contents in a bank—drawers *(d)*, stacks *(s)*, and loose money.

3. Distribute the pictures of the five banks, and have students record the algebraic expressions of what is in each bank.
4. Have the students work through the problems on the page, referring to the pictures and recording algebraically what they are thinking.
5. Discuss with the students how the algebraic representations allowed them to efficiently solve the problems.
6. Have the students reinforce and practice the concepts they have learned on the second page.

Part Two
1. Explain the context to the students, making sure they understand that a bank might have multiple vaults with identical contents inside. Focus their attention to the picture on the student page and have them discuss how the example equations represent what is pictured.
2. Have the students work through the problems on the page, drawing sketches if needed and recording algebraically what they are thinking.
3. Discuss with the students how the algebraic representations allowed them to efficiently solve the problems. Inform them that the process they are following is called the distributive property.
4. Have the students reinforce and practice the concepts they have learned on the second page.

Connecting Learning
1. How is what is in the picture represented in your expression? [type of content with a variable, number of contents with a coefficient]
2. What did you have to do with your algebra expressions to get the total contents of the two banks? [Add or subtract the number of drawers with drawers, number of stacks with stacks, and amount of loose money with money.]
3. How do you determine what is in a bank that has vaults? [Multiply the number of vaults by the amount of each type of content.]
4. Have students look at some simplifying expressions and distributive property problems in their textbooks. How are these problems like bank problems? Can you translate these problems into bank stories?

Extension
Have students develop their own bank problems. Have them write the story on one side of a paper and on the back side provide a key with the algebraic expressions showing the solution. Have students exchange or share their stories and solve them.

Solutions
Part One—A
First Bank = $10d + 8s + 20$
Federal Bank = $5d + 6s + 10$
Golden Bank = $3d + 6s + 8$
City Bank = $12d + 20s + 25$
National Bank = $8d + 12s + 15$

1. $15d + 14s + 30$
2. $15d + 26s + 33$
3. $2d + 12s + 5$
4. $8d + 12s + 18$
5. $18d + 20s + 35$
6. $5d + 2s + 10$
7. $20d + 32s + 40$
8. $13d + 18s + 25$
9. $4d + 8s + 10$
10. $13d + 14s + 28$

Part One—B
Valley Bank = $12d + 15s + 30$
Delta Bank = $15d + 25s + 50$
Lakeside Bank = $9d + 24s + 20$
River Bank = $6d + 12s + 30$
Summit Bank = $8d + 16s + 32$
Capitol Bank = $10d + 20s + 30$

1. $4d + 8s$
2. $3d + 10s + 20$
3. $20d + 31s + 62$
4. $3d + 6s + 15$
5. $33d + 61s + 112$
6. $6d + 2s + 10$
7. $8d + 24s + 40$
8. $10d + 15s + 5$

Part Two—A
1. $5(5d + 5s + 25) = 25d + 25s + 125$
2. $7(2d + 3s + 8) = 14d + 21s + 56$
3. $3(3d + 3s + 3) + 5(8s + 12)$
   $9d + 9s + 9 + 40s + 60$
   $9d + 49s + 69$
4. $4(7d + 5s + 20) - (2d + 12s + 50)$
   $28d + 20s + 80 - 2d - 12s - 50$
   $26d + 8s + 30$
5. $2(8d + 10s + 24) + 4(2d + 5s + 12)$
   $16d + 20s + 48 + 8d + 20s + 48$
   $24d + 40s + 96$
6. $5(6d + 5s + 15) - 3(5d + 5s + 5)$
   $30d + 25s + 75 - 15d - 15s - 15$
   $15d + 10s + 60$

Part Two—B
Valley Bank = $12d + 15s + 30$
Delta Bank = $15d + 25s + 50$
Lakeside Bank = $10d + 20s + 30$
River Bank = $6d + 12s + 30$)
Summit Bank = $20d + 20s + 100$
Capitol Bank = $20d + 32s + 80$

1. $5(3d + 5s + 10) + (8s + 15) = 15d + 33s + 65$
2. $4(5d + 8s + 20) + 3(4d + 5s + 10) =$
   $32d + 47s + 110$
3. $\dfrac{2(3d + 6s + 15)}{3} = 2d + 4s + 10$
4. $5(4d + 4s + 20) - (12d + 50) = 8d + 20s + 50$

WHAT'S IN THE BANK?

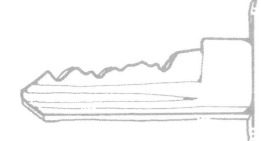

Key Question

How can you use symbols to keep track of what's in the bank?

Learning Goals

Students will:

- translate the contents of a bank into algebraic expressions,

- symbolically combine the contents of several banks to conceptualize combining of like terms, and

- develop an understanding of the distributive property by considering the contents of like vaults in a bank.

3

WHAT'S IN THE BANK?

FIRST BANK

FEDERAL BANK

GOLDEN BANK

CITY BANK

NATIONAL BANK

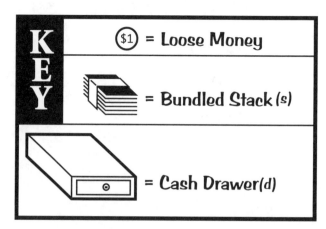

KEY	
$1	= Loose Money
	= Bundled Stack (s)
	= Cash Drawer (d)

4

WHAT'S IN THE BANK?

PART ONE · A

Banks have drawers of money *(d)*,

bundled stacks of money *(s)*,

and loose money. $1

Change each picture into an algebraic expression of what's in the bank.

First Bank = $10d + 8s + 20$

Federal Bank = _____

Golden Bank = _____

City Bank = _____

National Bank = _____

1. What are the combined contents of **First Bank** and **Federal Bank**?

2. What are the combined contents of **Golden Bank** and **City Bank**?

3. What is the difference in contents of **City Bank** and **First Bank**?

4. What are the combined contents of **Federal Bank** and **Golden Bank**?

5. What are the combined contents of **First Bank** and **National Bank**?

6. What is the difference in contents of **First Bank** and **Federal Bank**?

7. What are the combined contents of **City Bank** and **National Bank**?

8. What are the combined contents of **Federal Bank** and **National Bank**?

9. What is the difference in contents of **City Bank** and **National Bank**?

10. What are the combined contents of **First Bank** and **Golden Bank**?

WHAT'S IN THE BANK?

Record the description of each bank's contents algebraically.

Valley Bank has 12 drawers, 15 stacks, and $30.

Delta Bank has 15 drawers, 25 stacks, and $50.

Lakeside Bank has 9 drawers, 24 stacks, and $20.

River Bank has 6 drawers, 12 stacks, and $30.

Summit Bank has 8 drawers, 16 stacks, and $32.

Capitol Bank has 10 drawers, 20 stacks, and $30.

Use the algebraic expression of each bank's contents to solve the problems.

1. What is the difference in the contents of **River Bank** and **Capitol Bank**?

2. What is the difference in the contents of **Valley Bank** and **Delta Bank**?

3. **Valley Bank** and **Summit Bank** merge to become **County Bank**. What are the contents of **County Bank**?

4. **River Bank** splits its contents evenly between two branches. What are the contents of each branch?

5. **Summit**, **Capitol**, and **Delta Banks** merge to become **State Bank**. What are the contents of **State Bank**?

6. In a bank robbery, 10 stacks and 20 dollars are stolen from **River Bank**. What's left in the bank?

7. A deposit of eight stacks and eight dollars is made to **Summit Bank**. What's in the bank?

8. A withdrawal of two drawers and 25 dollars is made at **Valley Bank**. What's in the bank?

6

WHAT'S IN THE BANK?

Record the description of each bank's contents algebraically. Then condense (simplify) the account so it tells the quantity of drawers, stacks, and loose money in the bank.

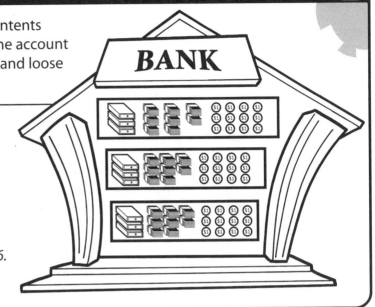

Example:

The bank has 3 vaults. Each vault contains 3 drawers, 8 stacks, and $12. What's in the bank?

$3(3d + 8s + 12) = B$
$9d + 24s + 36 = B$
The bank has 9 drawers, 24 stacks, and $36.

---

1. The bank has 5 vaults. Each vault contains 5 drawers, 5 stacks, and $25. What's in the bank?

2. The bank has 7 vaults. Each vault contains 2 drawers, 3 stacks, and $8. What's in the bank?

3. The bank has 3 vaults with 3 drawers, 3 stacks, and $3, and 5 other vaults with no drawers, 8 stacks, and $12. What's in the bank?

4. The bank had 4 vaults with 7 drawers, 5 stacks, and $20. The bank was robbed, and 2 drawers, 12 stacks and $50 were taken. What's in the bank?

5. One bank has 2 vaults. Each vault contains 8 drawers, 10 stacks, and $24. A second bank has 4 vaults, and each vault contains 2 drawers, 5 stacks, and $12. The two banks merge into one. What's in the bank?

6. The first bank had 5 vaults. Each vault contains 6 drawers, 5 stacks, and $15. A second bank opens and fills each of its 3 vaults with 5 drawers, 5 stacks, and $5 from the first bank. What's left in the first bank?

Make up your own *What's in the Bank?* problem to give to another student. Make a key that shows the steps to find the correct solution.

SOLVING EQUATIONS: A CONCEPTUAL APPROACH

WHAT'S IN THE BANK?

PART TWO · B

Use the algebraic expression describing what is in each bank to determine what's in the bank.

Valley Bank = $3(4d + 5s + 10)$ **Delta Bank** = $5(3d + 5s + 10)$

Lakeside Bank = $2(5d + 10s + 15)$ **River Bank** = $2(3d + 6s + 15)$

Summit Bank = $5(4d + 4s + 20)$ **Capitol Bank** = $4(5d + 8s + 20)$

Simplify each expression and then make up a "bank story" to go with each problem.

1. $5(3d + 5s + 10) + (8s + 15)$

2. $4(5d + 8s + 20) + 3(4d + 5s + 10)$

3. $\dfrac{2(3d + 6s + 15)}{3}$

4. $5(4d + 4s + 20) - (12d + 50)$

SOLVING EQUATIONS   8   © 2007 AIMS Education Foundation

WHAT'S IN THE BANK?

Connecting Learning

1. How is what is in the picture represented in your expression?

2. What did you have to do with your algebra expressions to get the total contents of the two banks?

3. How do you determine what is in a bank that has vaults?

4. Look at some simplifying expressions and distributive property problems in your textbook. How are these problems like bank problems? Can you translate these problems into bank stories?

WIDGETS, INC.

Topic
Mathematical properties

Key Question
How can you use symbols to keep inventory of items shipped and received at a loading dock?

Learning Goals
Students will:
- translate a description of what is on a loading dock to algebraic symbols;
- simulate shipping and receiving on a loading dock and keep track of changes with algebraic symbols; and
- learn to use the commutative, associative, and distributive properties to keep inventory with algebraic symbols.

Guiding Documents
Project 2061 Benchmark
- *Mathematicians often represent things with abstract ideas, such as numbers or perfectly straight lines, and then work with those ideas alone. The "things" from which they abstract can be ideas themselves (for example, a proposition about "all equal-sided triangles" or "all odd numbers").*

NCTM Standards 2000*
- *Use the associative and commutative properties of addition and multiplication and the distributive property of multiplication over addition to simplify computations with integers, fractions, and decimals*
- *Develop an initial conceptual understanding of different uses of variables*
- *Use symbolic algebra to represent situations and to solve problems, especially those that involve linear relationships*

Math
Number
    distributive property
    commutative property
Algebra
    variables
    simplifying expressions

Integrated Processes
Observing
Comparing and contrasting
Generalizing
Applying

Materials
Widgets Intro animation (see *Management 2*)
Widget models (see *Management 3*)
Scissors
Student pages

Background Information
Learning and using the associative, commutative, and distributive properties often causes difficulty for students for several reasons. First, in numbers, the properties seem so obvious as a result of students' primary education. When the algebraic symbol of a variable or unknown is added, students have no intuitive understanding of how x and x^2 differ, and as a result often combine them. Using a physical context provides an environment that encourages students to develop a meaning for these symbolic manipulations.

This context has students keep track of the items on a loading dock. Widgets are placed in individual boxes whose quantities are kept track of by a number. Packs are sets of widget boxes bound in single-file strings of unidentified length. Since the length of a pack varies, the variable (P) is assigned to mean a pack. $4P$ would symbolize four packs. Packs are bound in square pallets. A pallet is square with a width of the undefined length of a pack so it is symbolized as a P square (P^2).

As students make sets of materials ready for shipping or receiving, they become familiar with the difference between P (packs) and P^2 (pallets). As they combine sets, they sort the materials into like groups. As a result, students become familiar with combining like terms in symbols. In sorting the materials, the students often reverse the positions of items to get single piles of like materials. As students record what they act out, they become familiar with how the commutative and distributive properties look symbolically. It becomes quite natural to ungroup sets so they can change position to be reassociated in like groups, as shown in the following example.

$(5P + 3) + (2P + 4)$
$5P + 3 + 2P + 4$
$5P + 2P + 3 + 4$
$(5P + 2P) + (3 + 4)$
$7P + 7$

When two sets of materials are received, they are combined. This models addition. When a shipment is taken away from a set of materials, this models subtraction.

When a pallet is short packs, or a pack is short units, this models the use of subtraction as a negative situation. A pallet short two packs would be symbolized $P^2 - 2P$. A pack short a unit would be written $P - 1$. To show a missing pack or unit with the manipulatives, the missing pack or unit is covered by the same unit. To get a pallet or pack to be missing something, what is missing is taken out the package. When the pallet or pack missing something is taken away, what was taken out is left behind. Consider the problem $(5P + 3) - (2P - 2)$. As the two packs that are missing two units are taken away, the two units left behind increase the number of units.

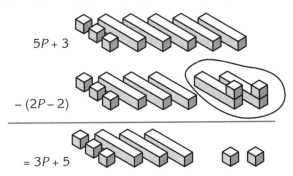

$5P + 3$

$- (2P - 2)$

$= 3P + 5$

When adding sets that are missing units with the manipulatives, missing units are matched with available units. Consider the problem $(2P + 3) + (3P - 2)$.

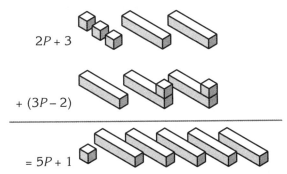

$2P + 3$

$+ (3P - 2)$

$= 5P + 1$

Two of the missing units are paired with available units, representing the available units filling the space in the packs. The paired units are removed because they have been used to complete the packs.

Multiplication and the distributive property are modeled by loads on a forklift. For three loads of two pallets missing one pack, the students would make three piles of two P^2s with one P on top. Combining them would make one pile of six P^2s with three Ps on top. The algebraic equation would be $3(2P^2 - P) = 6P^2 - 3P$.

Division is modeled by splitting up a large shipment evenly between forklifts. A large set is made and then fair shares are made with each of the forklift loads being the same size. The symbolic representation for a shipment of 12 pallets, 15 packs, and 27 units split into three forklift loads would be written: $(12P^2 + 15P + 27) \div 3 = 4P^2 + 5P + 9$. Division of a large of set of things into smaller sets of equal amounts is really just undoing distribution, or distribution backward.

Management

1. The teacher instruction video *Part One: Contexts for Thinking* is on the accompanying DVD. It is also available at the following URL: www.aimsedu. org/media/books/. It provides the rationale and suggestions for using this activity successfully in your classroom.

2. The animation *Widgets Intro* is on the accompanying DVD and at the URL listed above. Make preparations in your classroom so students can view the animation. If viewing through a computer, a projector enhances the experience.

3. Copy the page of widgets, packs, and pallets onto card stock. Each group of two to four students needs one copy of this page to cut out. If you have algebra tiles, those can be used instead of the widget models.

4. This investigation is made of four distinct activities. Each should be completed as an individual lesson. The math concepts developed with each are listed here.
   Shipping Widgets: associative and commutative properties, combining like terms, addition and subtraction of terms
   Loads of Widgets: Distributive property, multiplication
   Shipping Inventory: Reinforcement of concepts
   Level Loads: Division of expressions

5. Dealing with negatives with manipulatives can be problematic for students. Many teachers find it is sufficient to develop understanding using manipulatives with positive situations only. Introduction of negative situations can take place at the symbolic level applying the understanding gained with the manipulatives. The first pages of *Shipping Widgets* and *Loads of Widgets* have problems with only positive situations. Negative situations are isolated on the second or third pages. Consider what will work best for the needs of your students.

Procedure

1. If available, show the students the *Widgets Intro* animation.

2. Distribute widget materials or algebra tiles to each group of students.

3. Explain the scenario to the students, and as a class work through the first problem or two to make sure students understand what they are to do.

4. Have students work through all the problems by first acting them out with the manipulatives and then recording with algebraic symbols what they did.

5. When all the students have completed the problems, discuss their solutions and generalize strategies for completing other similar problems with only symbols.

Connecting Learning

1. With the materials, what did you do to make an inventory when several sets of materials were combined? [moved them into like piles before counting]
2. The commutative property means you can move things around. In other words, order does not matter in addition and multiplication. What did you do with the materials that demonstrates the commutative property? [moved the materials to put them in a different arrangement or order]
3. The associative property states that with a string of addends or factors, you can group the terms in pairs using parentheses any way you like. What did you do with the materials that demonstrates the associative property? [put like kinds of materials in a pile, grouped or sorted the materials]
4. How can you determine the total shipment if you know how many loads of the same size were delivered? [multiply the number of loads by the number of each of the items in a load]
5. How does the delivery of multiple loads of the same size demonstrate the distributive property? [The number of loads is multiplied by the number of each of the types of items. This is like distributing papers to every student in a class.]
6. How is dividing a large set of materials to make level loads like determining the inventory from multiple loads of the same size? [It is undoing multiple loads; you divide the number of each type of thing by the same number; it is the distributive property backward.]

Extensions

1. Allow students to use the algebra tile materials to work out similar problems out of their textbooks.
2. Have students develop similar problems of their own along with the solutions to share with other students in the class.

Solutions

Shipping Widgets

1. $(4P + 10) + (6P + 5) = 10P + 15$
2. $(3P^2 + 4P + 5) + (P^2 + 2P + 4) = 4P^2 + 6P + 9$
3. $(4P^2 + 2P + 3) + (3P + 4) = 4P^2 + 5P + 7$
4. $(P^2 + 5P + 7) + (2P^2 + 2P + 3) = 3P^2 + 7P + 10$
5. $(3P^2 + 8P + 12) - (2P^2 + 8P + 6) = P^2 + 6$
6. $(5P^2 + 5P + 5) - (3P^2 + 4P + 5) = 2P^2 + P$
7. $(4P + 10) - (4P + 5) = 5$
8. $(4P^2 - 5P) + (9P + 8) = 4P^2 + 4P + 8$
9. $(6P^2 + 3P + 5) + (P^2 - 4P) = 7P^2 - P + 5$
10. $(4P^2 + 3P + 2) + (2P^2 - 3P) = 6P^2 + 2$
11. $(6P^2 + 4P + 6) - (5P^2 + 4P + 5) = P^2 + 1$
12. $(6P^2 + 9P) - (4P^2 - 8P) = 2P^2 + 17P$
13. $(8P^2 + 4P + 2) - (4P^2 - 2P) = 4P^2 + 6P + 2$
14. $(4P + 8) - (4P - 4) = 12$

Loads of Widgets

1. $3(2P^2 + 3P + 4) + 2(3P^2 + 2P + 4) =$
   $6P^2 + 9P + 12 + 6P^2 + 4P + 8 = 12P^2 + 13P + 20$
2. $3(3P^2 + 2) + 4(4P + 2) =$
   $9P^2 + 6 + 16P + 8 = 9P^2 + 16P + 14$
3. $3(2P^2 + 4P + 2) + 2(3P^2 + 2P + 3) =$
   $6P^2 + 12P + 6 + 6P^2 + 4P + 6 = 12P^2 + 16P + 12$
4. $5(2P^2 + 3P + 4) + 2(2P + 3) =$
   $10P^2 + 15P + 20 + 4P + 6 = 10P^2 + 19P + 26$
5. $5(P^2 + 2P + 3) - 2(5P + 6) =$
   $5P^2 + 10P + 15 - 10P - 12 = 5P^2 + 3$
6. $3(2P^2 + 3P + 4) - 4(P^2 + 2P + 3) =$
   $6P^2 + 9P + 12 - 4P^2 - 8P - 12 = 2P^2 + P$
7. $3(2P^2 + 2P + 3) - 2(2P^2 + 3P + 4) =$
   $6P^2 + 6P + 9 - 4P^2 - 6P - 8 = 2P^2 + 1$
8. $2(4P^2 + 3P + 5) - 3(2P^2 + 2P + 3) =$
   $8P^2 + 6P + 10 - 6P^2 - 6P - 9 = 2P^2 + 1$
9. $4(P^2 + 2P + 2) + 2(3P^2 + 4P) =$
   $4P^2 + 8P + 8 + 6P^2 + 8P = 10P^2 + 16P + 8$
10. $3(2P^2 + 3P + 4) + 2(3P + 2) =$
    $6P^2 + 9P + 12 + 6P + 4 = 6P^2 + 15P + 16$
11. $4(2P^2 + 2P + 2) + 2(3P - 4) =$
    $8P^2 + 8P + 8 + 6P - 8 = 8P^2 + 14P$
12. $4(P^2 + 3P + 2) - 2(5P - 3) =$
    $4P^2 + 12P + 8 - 10P + 6 = 4P^2 + 2P + 14$
13. $2(3P^2 + 2) - 4(P^2 - 2P) =$
    $6P^2 + 4 - 4P^2 + 8P = 2P^2 + 8P + 4$
14. $5(P^2 + 2P + 3) - 3(3P - 2) =$
    $5P^2 + 10P + 15 - 9P + 6 = 5P^2 + P + 21$
15. $2(3P^2 + 3P + 4) + 3(3P - 2) =$
    $6P^2 + 6P + 8 + 9P - 6 = 6P^2 + 15P + 2$

Shipping Inventory

Load	Contents	Total Change	Loading Dock Inventory
+ 5	$5P^2 + 10P + 8$	$25P^2 + 50P + 40$	$25P^2 + 50P + 40$
+ 2	$2P^2 + 2P + 5$	$4P^2 + 4P + 10$	$29P^2 + 54P + 50$
− 4	$3P^2 + 6P + 5$	$-12P^2 - 24P - 20$	$17P^2 + 30P + 30$
+ 3	$3P^2 + 2P - 3$	$9P^2 + 6P - 9$	$26P^2 + 36P + 21$
− 2	$5P^2 + 8P + 4$	$-10P^2 - 16P - 8$	$16P^2 + 20P + 13$
− 4	$P^2 + 2P - 3$	$-4P^2 - 8P + 12$	$12P^2 + 12P + 25$
+ 3	$2P^2 - 3P + 1$	$6P^2 - 9P + 3$	$18P^2 + 3P + 28$
+ 6	$P^2 + 3P$	$6P^2 + 18P$	$24P^2 + 21P + 28$
− 3	$3P^2 + 5P + 2$	$-9P^2 - 15P - 6$	$15P^2 + 6P + 22$
− 4	$3P^2 + P + 5$	$-12P^2 - 4P - 20$	$3P^2 + 2P + 2$

Level Loads

Delivery Inventory	Number of Loads	Load Description
$12P^2 + 15P + 27$	$\div 3 =$	$4P^2 + 5P + 9$
$24P^2 + 12P + 16$	$\div 4 =$	$6P^2 + 3P + 4$
$14P^2 + 18P + 34$	$\div 2 =$	$7P^2 + 9P + 17$
$15P^2 + 25P + 35$	$\div 5 =$	$3P^2 + 5P + 7$
$21P^2 + 18P - 15$	$\div 3 =$	$7P^2 + 6P - 5$
$14P^2 + 6P + 16$	$\div 2 =$	$7P^2 + 3P + 8$
$14P^2 + 35P + 21$	$\div 7 =$	$2P^2 + 5P + 3$
$36P^2 + 8P - 28$	$\div 4 =$	$9P^2 + 2P - 7$
$33P^2 + 24P + 18$	$\div 3 =$	$11P^2 + 8P + 6$
$15P^2 - 10P + 35$	$\div 5 =$	$3P^2 - 2P + 7$

* Reprinted with permission from *Principles and Standards for School Mathematics*, 2000 by the National Council of Teachers of Mathematics. All rights reserved.

WIDGETS, INC.

Key Question

How can you use symbols to keep inventory of items shipped and received at a loading dock?

Learning Goals

Students will:

- translate a description of what is on a loading dock to algebraic symbols;

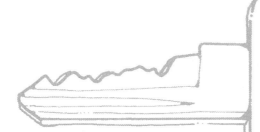

- simulate shipping and receiving on a loading dock and keep track of changes with algebraic symbols; and

- learn to use the commutative, associative, and distributive properties to keep inventory with algebraic symbols.

WIDGETS, INC.

14

WIDGETS, INC.

Stores receive widgets in packs. Packs are formed by widget cubes being bound together in a long string. The shipping supervisor is really only concerned with how many packs are sent or received so packs is shortened to (P). What is pictured below is recorded as $4P$.

Widgets, Inc. manufactures the ever-popular widget that is individually wrapped in a cubic box. Since widgets are the only things shipped, the shipping supervisor simply records the number of widgets for units shipped. What is pictured below is recorded as 5.

For larger shipments, packs are bound together in pallets. Pallets are formed as square flats that are one pack long and one pack wide. The dimensions of a pallet are $P \times P$ or P^2. The supervisor refers to pallets as a "pack squared." What is pictured below is recorded as $3P^2$.

DOCK:
$3P^2 + 4P + 5$

$3P^2 + 4P + 5$ is the shipping supervisor's accounting for what is pictured above.

WIDGETS, INC.

W INC.

Now, act as the shipping supervisor. Use your model units, packs, and pallets to act out what is shipped and received. Then make an accounting of what is on the loading dock using symbols.

Shipping/Receiving Invoice

1.
a. Received four packs and 10 units.
+
b. Received five units and six packs.
=
c. What is on the loading dock?

2.
a. Received three pallets, four packs, and five units.
+
b. Received four units, two packs, and one pallet.
=
c. What is on the loading dock?

3.
a. Received four pallets, two packs, and three units.
+
b. Received four units and three packs.
=
c. What is on the loading dock?

4.
a. Received a pallet, five packs, and seven units.
+
b. Received two pallets, three units, and two packs.
=
c. What is on the loading dock?

5.
a. Received three pallets, eight packs, and 12 units.
−
b. Shipped six units, two pallets, and eight packs.
=
c. What is on the loading dock?

6.
a. Received five pallets, five packs, and five units.
−
b. Shipped five units, four packs, and three pallets.
=
c. What is on the loading dock?

7.
a. Received four packs and 10 units.
−
b. Shipped five units and four packs.
=
c. What is on the loading dock?

WIDGETS, INC.

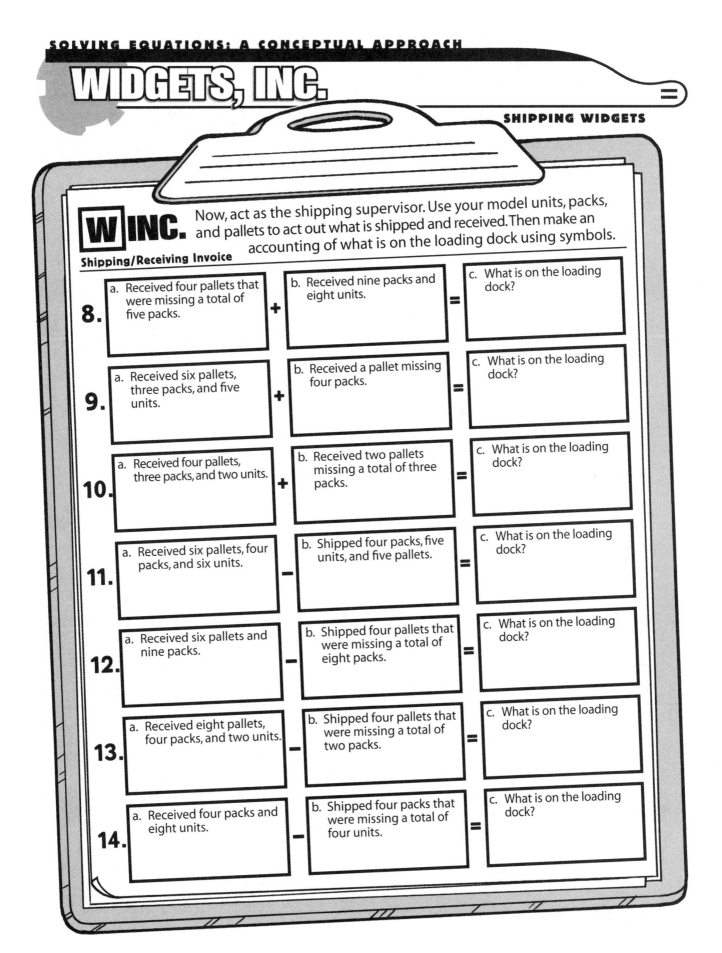

W INC.

Now, act as the shipping supervisor. Use your model units, packs, and pallets to act out what is shipped and received. Then make an accounting of what is on the loading dock using symbols.

Shipping/Receiving Invoice

8.
a. Received four pallets that were missing a total of five packs.
+
b. Received nine packs and eight units.
=
c. What is on the loading dock?

9.
a. Received six pallets, three packs, and five units.
+
b. Received a pallet missing four packs.
=
c. What is on the loading dock?

10.
a. Received four pallets, three packs, and two units.
+
b. Received two pallets missing a total of three packs.
=
c. What is on the loading dock?

11.
a. Received six pallets, four packs, and six units.
−
b. Shipped four packs, five units, and five pallets.
=
c. What is on the loading dock?

12.
a. Received six pallets and nine packs.
−
b. Shipped four pallets that were missing a total of eight packs.
=
c. What is on the loading dock?

13.
a. Received eight pallets, four packs, and two units.
−
b. Shipped four pallets that were missing a total of two packs.
=
c. What is on the loading dock?

14.
a. Received four packs and eight units.
−
b. Shipped four packs that were missing a total of four units.
=
c. What is on the loading dock?

WIDGETS, INC.

To receive and send shipments efficiently, multiple loads of the same size are made at the dock. A single forklift might make multiple loads, or multiple forklifts may take identical loads.

One forklift might be assigned to receive three loads of two pallets and two packs from a truck and put it on a loading dock.

$$3(2P^2 + 2P) = 6P^2 + 6P$$

Two forklifts might be assigned to each take three pallets and two packs and put them on trucks for shipping.

$$2(3P^2 + 2P) = 6P^2 + 4P$$

When both operations are done, there will be two packs left on the dock. Six pallets were received and shipped. Six packs were received, but only four were shipped, leaving two packs on the dock.

2P

WIDGETS, INC.

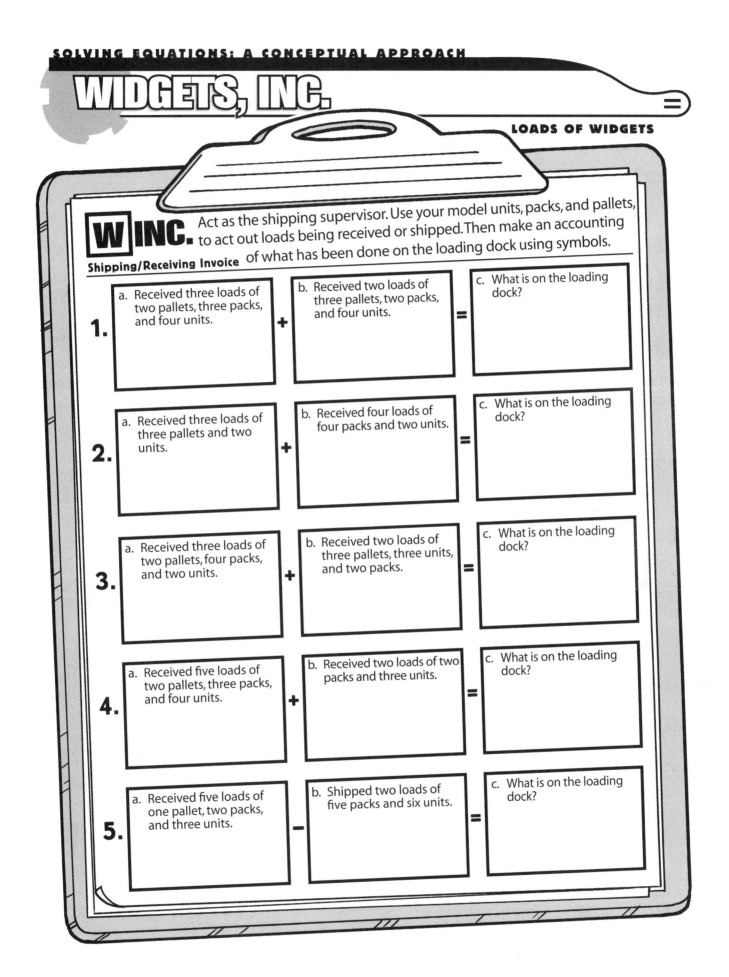

W INC. Act as the shipping supervisor. Use your model units, packs, and pallets, to act out loads being received or shipped. Then make an accounting of what has been done on the loading dock using symbols.

Shipping/Receiving Invoice

1.
a. Received three loads of two pallets, three packs, and four units.
+
b. Received two loads of three pallets, two packs, and four units.
=
c. What is on the loading dock?

2.
a. Received three loads of three pallets and two units.
+
b. Received four loads of four packs and two units.
=
c. What is on the loading dock?

3.
a. Received three loads of two pallets, four packs, and two units.
+
b. Received two loads of three pallets, three units, and two packs.
=
c. What is on the loading dock?

4.
a. Received five loads of two pallets, three packs, and four units.
+
b. Received two loads of two packs and three units.
=
c. What is on the loading dock?

5.
a. Received five loads of one pallet, two packs, and three units.
−
b. Shipped two loads of five packs and six units.
=
c. What is on the loading dock?

19

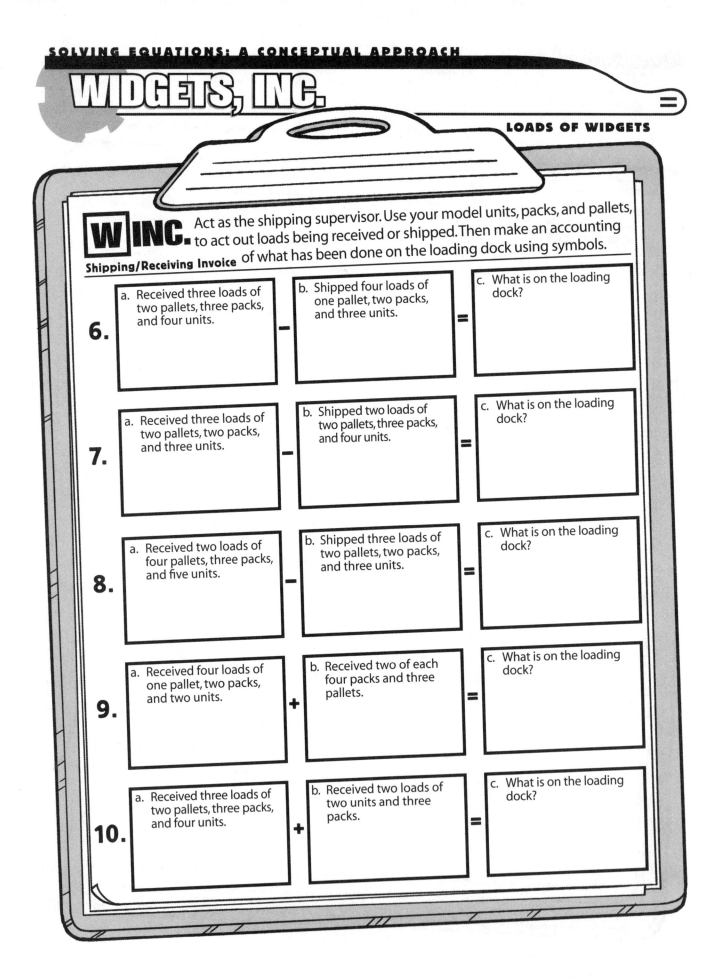

W INC.
Shipping/Receiving Invoice

Act as the shipping supervisor. Use your model units, packs, and pallets, to act out loads being received or shipped. Then make an accounting of what has been done on the loading dock using symbols.

6.
a. Received three loads of two pallets, three packs, and four units.
−
b. Shipped four loads of one pallet, two packs, and three units.
=
c. What is on the loading dock?

7.
a. Received three loads of two pallets, two packs, and three units.
−
b. Shipped two loads of two pallets, three packs, and four units.
=
c. What is on the loading dock?

8.
a. Received two loads of four pallets, three packs, and five units.
−
b. Shipped three loads of two pallets, two packs, and three units.
=
c. What is on the loading dock?

9.
a. Received four loads of one pallet, two packs, and two units.
+
b. Received two of each four packs and three pallets.
=
c. What is on the loading dock?

10.
a. Received three loads of two pallets, three packs, and four units.
+
b. Received two loads of two units and three packs.
=
c. What is on the loading dock?

WIDGETS, INC.

W INC.
Shipping/Receiving Invoice

Act as the shipping supervisor. Use your model units, packs, and pallets, to act out loads being received or shipped. Then make an accounting of what has been done on the loading dock using symbols.

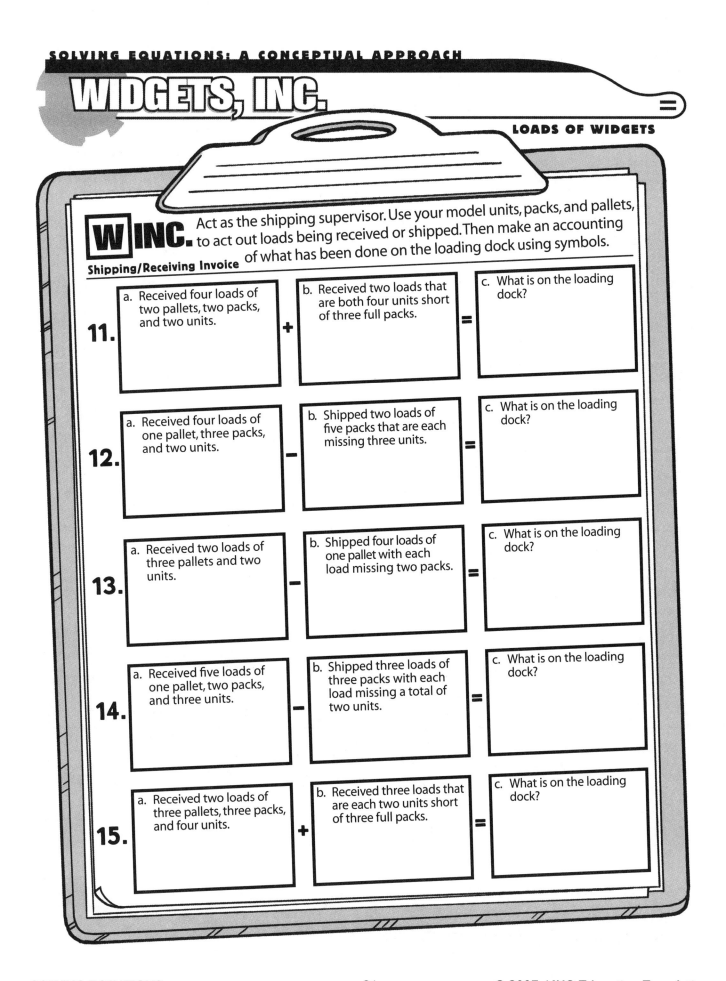

11.
a. Received four loads of two pallets, two packs, and two units.

+

b. Received two loads that are both four units short of three full packs.

=

c. What is on the loading dock?

12.
a. Received four loads of one pallet, three packs, and two units.

−

b. Shipped two loads of five packs that are each missing three units.

=

c. What is on the loading dock?

13.
a. Received two loads of three pallets and two units.

−

b. Shipped four loads of one pallet with each load missing two packs.

=

c. What is on the loading dock?

14.
a. Received five loads of one pallet, two packs, and three units.

−

b. Shipped three loads of three packs with each load missing a total of two units.

=

c. What is on the loading dock?

15.
a. Received two loads of three pallets, three packs, and four units.

+

b. Received three loads that are each two units short of three full packs.

=

c. What is on the loading dock?

21

WIDGETS, INC.

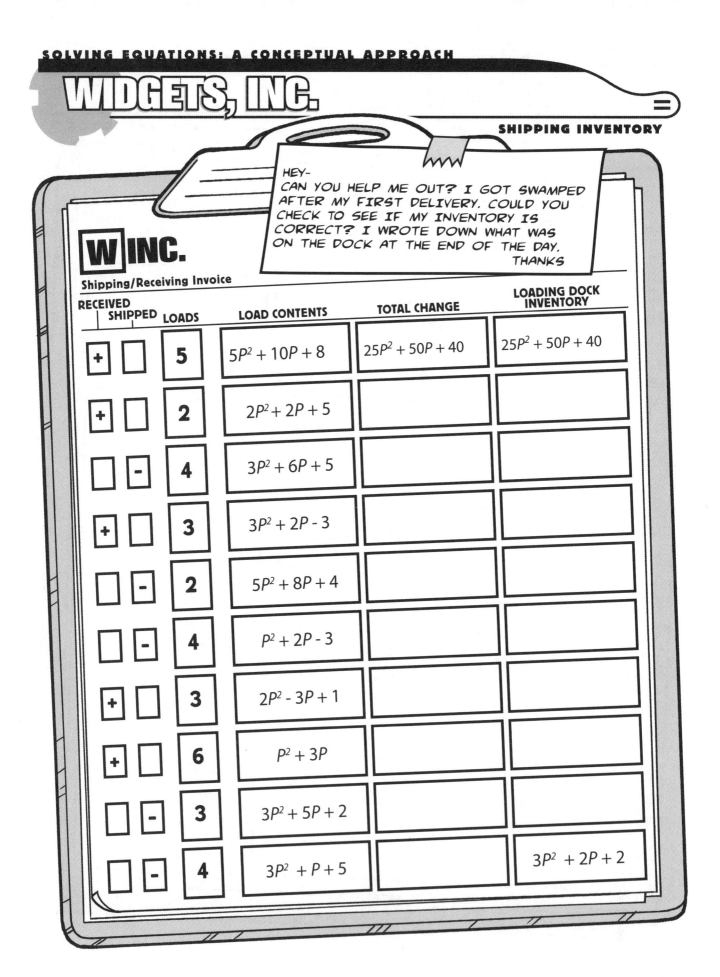

W INC.

Shipping/Receiving Invoice

HEY-
CAN YOU HELP ME OUT? I GOT SWAMPED
AFTER MY FIRST DELIVERY. COULD YOU
CHECK TO SEE IF MY INVENTORY IS
CORRECT? I WROTE DOWN WHAT WAS
ON THE DOCK AT THE END OF THE DAY.
                                    THANKS

RECEIVED	SHIPPED	LOADS	LOAD CONTENTS	TOTAL CHANGE	LOADING DOCK INVENTORY
+		5	$5P^2 + 10P + 8$	$25P^2 + 50P + 40$	$25P^2 + 50P + 40$
+		2	$2P^2 + 2P + 5$		
	−	4	$3P^2 + 6P + 5$		
+		3	$3P^2 + 2P - 3$		
	−	2	$5P^2 + 8P + 4$		
	−	4	$P^2 + 2P - 3$		
+		3	$2P^2 - 3P + 1$		
+		6	$P^2 + 3P$		
	−	3	$3P^2 + 5P + 2$		
	−	4	$3P^2 + P + 5$		$3P^2 + 2P + 2$

WIDGETS, INC.

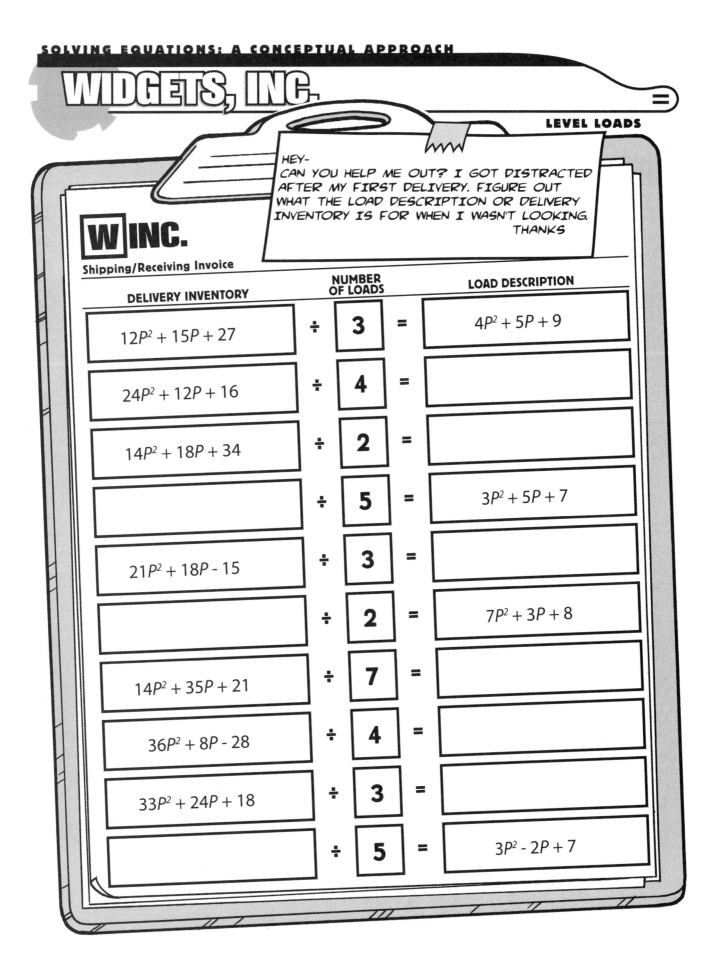

W INC.

Shipping/Receiving Invoice

HEY-
CAN YOU HELP ME OUT? I GOT DISTRACTED AFTER MY FIRST DELIVERY. FIGURE OUT WHAT THE LOAD DESCRIPTION OR DELIVERY INVENTORY IS FOR WHEN I WASN'T LOOKING.
THANKS

DELIVERY INVENTORY		NUMBER OF LOADS		LOAD DESCRIPTION
$12P^2 + 15P + 27$	÷	3	=	$4P^2 + 5P + 9$
$24P^2 + 12P + 16$	÷	4	=	
$14P^2 + 18P + 34$	÷	2	=	
	÷	5	=	$3P^2 + 5P + 7$
$21P^2 + 18P - 15$	÷	3	=	
	÷	2	=	$7P^2 + 3P + 8$
$14P^2 + 35P + 21$	÷	7	=	
$36P^2 + 8P - 28$	÷	4	=	
$33P^2 + 24P + 18$	÷	3	=	
	÷	5	=	$3P^2 - 2P + 7$

WIDGETS, INC.

Connecting Learning

1. With the materials, what did you do to make an inventory when several sets of materials were combined?

2. The commutative property means you can move things around. In other words, order does not matter in addition and multiplication. What did you do with the materials that demonstrates the commutative property?

3. The associative property states that with a string of addends or factors, you can group the terms in pairs using parentheses any way you like. What did you do with the materials that demonstrates the associative property?

WIDGETS, INC.

Connecting Learning

4. How can you determine the total shipment if you know how many loads of the same size were delivered?

5. How does the delivery of multiple loads of the same size demonstrate the distributive property?

6. How is dividing a large set of materials to make level loads like determining the inventory from multiple loads of the same size?

JUMPING TO SOLUTIONS

Topic
Solving equations

Key Questions
1. How can you determine the length of a jump by knowing the position of the jumper at two different times?
2. How does an equation describe how a person moved to a position?

Learning Goals
Students will:
- measure the position and number of jumps of a person,
- generate an equation that describes how the person got to the end position, and
- determine the length of the person's jump from the equation.

Guiding Documents
Project 2061 Benchmarks
- *An equation containing a variable may be true for just one value of the variable.*
- *Mathematical statements can be used to describe how one quantity changes when another changes. Rates of change can be computed from magnitudes and vice versa.*
- *The operations + and – are inverses of each other— one undoes what the other does; likewise x and ÷.*

NCTM Standards 2000*
- *Develop an initial conceptual understanding of different uses of variables*
- *Use symbolic algebra to represent situations and to solve problems, especially those that involve linear relationships*
- *Recognize and generate equivalent forms for simple algebraic expressions and solve linear equations*

Math
Algebra
  solving equations

Integrated Processes
Observing
Comparing and contrasting
Generalizing

Materials
Metric tape measure
2 markers (blocks, erasers)
Student pages

Background Information
Students need a concrete experience with which to relate their thinking. Jumping, hopping, and leaping provide very active experiences to which students relate their thinking. Having a student start jumping at a random position along a tape measure and then measuring the student's position after a number of jumps provides the context for an equation. This meaningful context allows students to develop a conceptual understanding of the meaning of an equation and how to solve it.

Consider the example where a student starts at the 1.2-meter mark on a tape measure, takes four jumps, and is at 4.4 meters. When students are asked to draw a sketch and describe how the jumper got to the 4.4-meter position, their sketches look like this.

1.2   4.4

They explain, "The jumper started at 1.2 meters and jumped four times to end at 4.4." This description clearly translates into the equation $1.2 + 4J = 4.4$ where J represents the length of the jumps. It is not hard for students to recognize that this is equivalent to the form $4J + 1.2 = 4.4$ found in their math texts. This form might be translated "four jumps and 1.2 meters is 4.4 meters."

Now the question "What is a jump (J)?" or "How long is a jump?" naturally arises. When students are posed this question, they need to be given time to ponder how this can be determined. Because of the experience and context surrounding the question, students can generally grapple with the numbers to come up with the solution. As students share their thinking, they will clarify what they did and will help those students having difficulty. When students clearly understand what they are doing, it can then be modeled in algebraic form. As students work through the context numerous times, they will be able to deal with more abstraction until they can work similar problems symbolically with no reference to a context.

Following is a typical discussion in a classroom:

Teacher:
"Now we have the equation about Patrick's jumping—1.2 + 4J = 4.4 The J in the equation represents jumps. So how long is a jump? Use your sketch, numbers, or an equation to figure this out." The teacher than allows students ample time to grapple with the question on their own. As students start to find the solution, the teacher suggests they share with a partner their methods of solution. This allows others time to find a solution or provides a chance for the struggling student to make progress toward a solution. When it is evident that most of the class has found a solution, the teacher asks, "How many of you found a solution or think you have made a good start?" As most or all of the class raises their hands, the teacher has encouraged participation. "Great! Who knows what they did to get started?" Almost all the hands remain up, and the students are feeling successful. "Who would like to share with the class what they did to get started?" By asking for volunteers, no one is put on the spot and all the students remain engaged.

Danny:
Crosses out the beginning of the tape on the sketch on the board and says, "I got rid of this."

Teacher:
"Why did you do that?" is asked to see what Danny is really thinking.

Danny:
"We want to know about the jumps, so we need to get rid of the 'head start.'"

Teacher:
"How many understand why Danny wants to get rid of this starting position?" Most students respond with a hand. "How many of you did something like Danny and got rid of the starting distance?" Some students raise their hands while others look puzzled. "Did you all do what Danny did and just cross out the start, or is there something to do with the numbers?

Janet:
"I just took away the starting number and got 3.2."

Teacher:
"Can you write that as a number sentence?" Janet writes 4.4 − 1.2 = 3.2. "Thanks, Janet. Now does everyone see where Janet got this number? Why is she doing this?"

Miguel:
"She has the finish and she is taking away the 'head start.'"

Teacher:
"So, what does Janet's answer of 3.2 tell us about Patrick's jumping?"

Katie:
"It's how far he jumped."

Teacher:
"So, Danny just crossed out the head start and Janet did an arithmetic problem. Can anyone explain how what Danny and Janet did are related?"

Olivia:
"Danny crossed out the head start to get the jump part and Janet subtracted the head start so it's only the jumps."

Teacher:
"Now we have seen how we can use the pictures or numbers to think about the problem, but we are supposed to be learning some algebra, so let me show you how we can think about what we have done with algebra. Here's the equation. Now Danny says get rid of the head start." The teacher crosses out the 1.2 in the equation.

$$\cancel{1.2} + 4J = 4.4$$

"But you can't just cross out numbers you don't want in the problem. To get rid of it, you need to subtract it. That's what Danny was thinking about, so we just do the subtraction on the description side of the equation."

$$\begin{array}{r} \cancel{1.2} + 4J = 4.4 \\ \underline{- 1.2 } \\ 4J = \end{array}$$

"Now, if you are going to get rid of the head start on the description side, you have to make the distance jumped shorter too. That's what Janet was doing with her subtraction."

$$\begin{array}{r} \cancel{1.2} + 4J = 4.4 \\ \underline{- 1.2 - 1.2} \\ 4J = 3.2 \end{array}$$

"So we took off the head start and know that four jumps are 3.2 meters. Now, how did you determine how long each of the four jumps are?"

Laura:
"The jumps in the picture split the distance into four pieces, so you split the 3.2 into four pieces too."

Teacher:
"So how do you split up numbers into four pieces?"

David:
"You divide 3.2 by four to get a jump. I got 0.8."

Teacher:
"Does everyone see why the four jumps split the distance into four equal pieces and why David divided 3.2 meters four ways to get a jump length? In algebra we can show this too. Laura suggested the four jumps divided the distance, so we divide the four jumps four ways. David divided the distance of 3.2 four ways too to get the distance of each jump."

$$\begin{array}{r} \cancel{1.2} + 4J = 4.4 \\ \underline{- 1.2 - 1.2} \\ 4J = 3.2 \\ \underline{\div 4 \div 4} \\ J = 0.8 \end{array}$$

To confirm the correct solution, the teacher brings the students' attention back to the tape measure. From the starting position, four 0.8 meters "jumps" were made to see that it did get the jumper to the 4.4-meter position.

As students work through problems thoughtfully at a conceptual level, they recognize why they are doing things mathematically and see the connection to the abstract algebra manipulation. Working through a number of similar problems in this context, students begin to translate equations with respect to the context and can reason to the solution with the support of the context. With continued practice, students move to abstract manipulation with no reference to the context but can always rebuild their understanding through the context.

Subtraction is introduced into equations by having the hopper start from a position before the start of the tape measure. A hopper starting at 0.6 meters before the tape and taking five hops to reach 2.9 meters is represented by the equation: $-0.6 + 5H = 5H - 0.6 = 2.9$. With this situation, the hopper hopped the 2.9 on the tape plus the 0.6 meter before the tape. Add 0.6 to both sides to show that $5H = 3.5$. Again a division by five expresses the length of a hop ($H = 0.7$).

Management

1. The animation *Part Two: Multiple Representations* is on the accompanying DVD. It is also available at the following URL: www.aimsedu.org/media/books/. Make preparations in your classroom so students can view the animation. If viewing through a computer, a projector enhances the experience.
2. An area for students to jump needs to be cleared before the activity. A wide aisle in the front or middle of the classroom works well. The area needs to be long enough for students to take seven to 10 jumps, hops, or leaps.
3. The best success is achieved when students are allowed to grapple with the situation and develop a meaningful solution on their own. Allow time for students to consider the problem and share their reasoning. If students make no progress on their own, have them follow the leading questions on the student page.
4. The best results come when the lengths of the jumps, hops, or leaps are consistent. Encourage the students not to go for the longest jump but to make the most consistent jumps. Different forms of jumping are listed on the student page to suggest that the value of the jumps should change and different variables would be used for each. The definition of each type can follow the illustration. A jump is on one foot; a hop uses both feet; and leaping involves bounding on alternating feet.

Procedure

1. Stretch out a tape measure across the length of the prepared jumping area.
2. Select three volunteers from the class—a jumper and two markers.
3. Place the jumper at a random position on the tape measure and have one of the volunteers place a marker behind the jumper's heel.
4. Have the jumper take three to seven jumps down the tape measure and have the second volunteer place a marker at the jumper's heels.
5. Instruct students to complete the sketch of the jump by starting on the X and drawing in the number of jumps taken. Have them record the measurements of the starting and ending positions.
6. Ask students to verbally describe how the jumper got to the ending position and develop an equation that is equivalent to the description.
7. Have students contemplate how to determine the length of each jump. If students make no progress on their own, pose leading questions using the student page.
8. Have students share with the class the different methods they used to determine the size of a jump.
9. Using a similar procedure, have students reinforce their thinking by measuring a hopping and leaping student. If it is appropriate, have the third hopper start before the tape measure so the students will be introduced to subtraction in the equation.
10. With the investigation as a context, have students make sketches and equations to solve similar contextual problems on the student pages.

Connecting Learning

1. Describe how the person got to the finish. [Beginning at the start position, the jumper made a number of jumps to get to the finish.]
2. How would you translate your verbal description into an equation? [start position + number of jumps = finish position]
3. Using your sketch, equation, or numbers, how would you determine the length of a jump?
   a. How many jumps did the jumper make?
   b. Where did the jumper start?
   c. Where did the jumper finish?
   d. How far did the jumper jump all together?
   e. How far did the jumper jump each time he or she jumped?
4. What steps did you follow every time to determine the length of a jump, hop, or leap?

Extensions

1. Have students write their own narratives about jumping situations and make a sketch, equation, and solution. Then have students share their narratives with each other, solve, and check.

28

2. Have students look at the two-step solving equations in their texts. Have them discuss the similarity between the equations in the book and equations from the situations. Have them translate the equations into jump situations and solve.

Solutions

Page Three

1. $12 + 5J = 27$
   $5J = 15$
   $J = 3$

2. $18 + 7H = 53$
   $7H = 35$
   $H = 5$

3. $12 + 9L = 39$
   $9L = 27$
   $L = 3$

4. $-14 + 12J = 10$
   $12J = 24$
   $J = 2$

5. $5 + 6H = 35$
   $6H = 30$
   $H = 5$

6. $7L + 6 = 20$
   $7L = 14$
   $L = 2$

Page Four

1. $15 + 4J = 43$
   $4J = 28$
   $J = 7$

2. $5H + 9 = 29$
   $5H = 20$
   $H = 4$

3. $-8 + 9L = 19$
   $9L = 27$
   $L = 3$

4. $23 + 3J = 35$
   $3J = 12$
   $J = 4$

5. $-10 + 6L = 20$
   $6L = 30$
   $L = 5$

6. $6H + 13 = 55$
   $6H = 42$
   $H = 7$

7. $45 + 7H = 59$
   $7H = 14$
   $H = 2$

8. $24 + 9L = 42$
   $9L = 18$
   $L = 2$

9. $6J + 15 = 33$
   $6J = 18$
   $J = 3$

10. $-5 + 4H = 23$
    $4H = 28$
    $H = 7$

11. $7J - 6 = 15$
    $7J = 21$
    $J = 3$

12. $3L - 7 = 20$
    $3L = 27$
    $L = 9$

*   Reprinted with permission from *Principles and Standards for School Mathematics*, 2000 by the National Council of Teachers of Mathematics. All rights reserved.

JUMPING TO SOLUTIONS

Key Questions

1. How can you determine the length of a jump by knowing the position of the jumper at two different times?
2. How does an equation describe how a person moved to a position?

Learning Goals

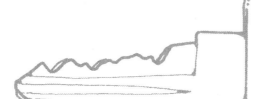

Students will:

- measure the position and number of jumps of a person,

- generate an equation that describes how the person got to the end position, and

- determine the length of the person's jump from the equation.

30

JUMPING TO SOLUTIONS

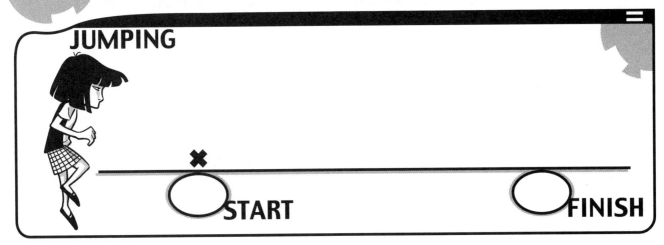

JUMPING

START   FINISH

1. Make a sketch of the jumps on the tape measure and record the start and finish position of the jumper.

2. Complete the sentence:

    The jumper starts at _____ centimeters, takes _____ jumps,

    and finishes at _____ centimeters.

3. Translate the sentence into an equation. Use *J* to represent a jump.

4. Use the sketch, numbers, and equation to determine the length of each jump.
    a. How far did the jumper move from start to finish? How do you get this number?

    b. How long was each of the jumps? How do you get this number?

JUMPING TO SOLUTIONS

HOPPING

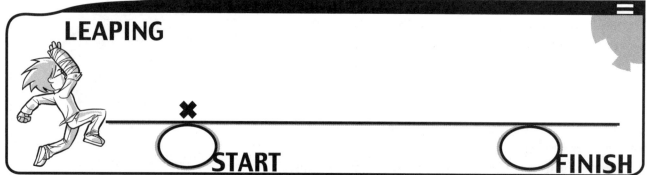

START   FINISH

1. Make a sketch of the hops on the line and record the start and finish position of the hopper.

2. Complete the sentence:

   The hopper starts at _____ centimeters, takes _____ hops, and finishes at _____ centimeters.

3. Translate the sentence into an equation. Use *H* to represent a hop.

4. Use the sketch, numbers, and equation to determine the length of each hop.

LEAPING

START   FINISH

1. Make a sketch of the leaps on the line and record the start and finish position of the leaper.

2. Complete the sentence:

   The leaper starts at _____ centimeters, takes _____ leaps, and finishes at _____ centimeters.

3. Translate the sentence into an equation. Use *L* to represent a leap.

4. Use the sketch, numbers, and equation to determine the length of each leap.

JUMPING TO SOLUTIONS

For each situation, make a sketch, write an equation, and determine the length of the jump, hop, or leap.

1. The student stands at the 12-foot mark and makes five jumps to finish at the 27-foot mark.

2. The frog is at the 18-inch mark and takes seven hops to finish at the 53-inch mark

3. The kangaroo is at the 12-yard line and takes nine leaps to finish at the 39-yard line.

4. The flea is 14 millimeters behind the start of the ruler and makes 12 jumps to finish at the 10-millimeter mark.

5. Starting at the five-foot mark, the grasshopper makes six hops to finish at the 35-foot mark.

6. The leaping lizard makes seven leaps to move from six inches to 20 inches.

33

JUMPING TO SOLUTIONS

Each of the equations describes a jumping, hopping, or leaping situation. Translate the equation back into English or make a sketch if it helps you make sense of the situation. Then use the equation to determine the length of a jump, hop, or leap.

1. $15 + 4J = 43$

2. $5H + 9 = 29$

3. $-8 + 9L = 19$

4. $23 + 3J = 35$

5. $-10 + 6L = 20$

6. $6H + 13 = 55$

7. $45 + 7H = 59$

8. $24 + 9L = 42$

9. $6J + 15 = 33$

10. $-5 + 4H = 23$

11. $7J - 6 = 15$

12. $3L - 7 = 20$

34

JUMPING TO SOLUTIONS

Connecting Learning

1. Describe how the person got to the finish.

2. How would you translate your verbal description into an equation?

3. Using your sketch, equation, or numbers, how would you determine the length of a jump?
   a. How many jumps did the jumper make?
   b. Where did the jumper start?
   c. Where did the jumper finish?
   d. How far did the jumper jump all together?
   e. How far did the jumper jump each time he or she jumped?

4. What steps did you follow every time to determine the length of a jump, hop, or leap?

35

TRACKING TREASURE ONE

Topic
Solving equations

Key Question
How do you use the clue to find the treasure?

Learning Goals
Students will:
- recognize that working backwards through an instruction leads to the original condition, and
- use inverse operations to solve one-step equations.

Guiding Documents
Project 2061 Benchmarks
- *Mathematics is the study of many kinds of patterns, including numbers and shapes and operations on them. Sometimes patterns are studied because they help to explain how the world works or how to solve practical problems, sometimes because they are interesting in themselves.*
- *In using mathematics, choices have to be made about what operations will give the best results. Results should always be judged by whether they make sense and are useful.*
- *Add, subtract, multiply, and divide whole numbers mentally, on paper, and with a calculator.*
- *State the purpose of each step in a calculation.*

NCTM Standards 2000*
- *Identify and use relationships between operations, such as division as the inverse of multiplication, to solve problems*
- *Describe, extend, and make generalizations about geometric and numeric patterns*
- *Represent the idea of a variable as an unknown quantity using a letter or a symbol*
- *Express mathematical relationships using equations*

Math
Number
    inverse operations
Algebra
    solving equations
        one-step equations

Integrated Processes
Observing
Comparing and contrasting
Generalizing
Applying

Materials
Tracks1 Intro animation (see *Management 2*)
Treasure track pages
Student pages
Envelopes

Background Information
To solve equations, students need to understand that to undo an operation, its inverse operation is used. To undo the operation of making two steps forward from a position $(x + 2)$, you just take two steps backward $(x + 2 - 2 = x)$.

Equality is the second idea required to solve equations. If two steps forward gets you to the seventh position $(x + 2 = 7)$, then taking away two steps will get you back to the original position $(x + 2 - 2 = 7 - 2)$. Since the instruction and the outcome are equal, when you take something from the instruction, you must do the same to the outcome to keep the equality. In our example, the original position was five $(x = 5)$. This investigation provides a context in which students can act out the situation. As students act out the problems, they develop an understanding of the meaning of the abstract record.

This investigation is based on the following scenario:

A pirate dug seven holes in a line and buried a chest in each hole. He put the treasure in one chest and locked it. He put the key and a clue in a second chest and locked it. He put the second key and a clue in a third chest and locked it. The pirate continued like this until he placed the sixth key and a clue in the seventh chest, but he did not lock the final chest. You have dug up the seven chests and have the key and clue from the unlocked chest. Your goal is to find the treasure. Be careful, because each lock is booby-trapped to explode and destroy all inside if the correct key is not used.

For the simulation, seven numbered sheets of folded paper are placed in order as a number line to represent the seven buried chests. In the first treasure track, chest seven is open with the following clue: $b + 2 = 7$. This instruction tells how the pirate got to this final chest. To get to chest seven, the pirate started at chest b and went forward two steps. To track back to b, you start at seven and go backwards two steps: $7 - 2 = b = 5$. The back of chest five is identified by b. Inside, the clue reads $5 \cdot c = 5$. The pirate got to chest five by multiplying the position of chest c by five.

Management

1. The teacher instruction video *Part Four: Inverse Operations* is on the accompanying DVD. It is also available at the following URL: www.aimsedu.org/media/books/. It provides the rationale and suggestions for using this activity successfully in your classroom.

2. The animation *Tracks1 Intro* is on the accompanying DVD and at the URL listed above. Make preparations in your classroom so students can view the animation. If viewing through a computer, a projector enhances the experience.

3. For *Part One,* make seven copies (per track) of the page with the large key and chest to use as whole class treasure tracks. Using the lines as guides, fold each page along the width and then the length so that the key ends up on the inside and the chest is on the outside. Use the lists below and write a number on each large chest, the corresponding letter on the back, and the appropriate clue on the inside.

Treasure Track One—Chest seven is open with clue.

Chest Number	Letter on Back	Inside Clue
1	c	$d - 5 = 1$
2	x	Treasure
3	e	$f - 1 = 3$
4	f	$x + 2 = 4$
5	b	$5 \cdot c = 5$
6	d	$2 \cdot e = 6$
7	a	$b + 2 = 7$

Treasure Track Two—Chest seven is open with clue.

Chest Number	Letter on Back	Inside Clue
1	c	$d - 4 = 1$
2	b	$2 \cdot c = 2$
3	f	$x - 1 = 3$
4	x	Treasure
5	d	$e - 1 = 5$
6	e	$2 \cdot f = 6$
7	a	$b + 5 = 7$

Treasure Track Three—Chest five is open with clue.

Chest Number	Letter on Back	Inside Clue
1	c	$d - 1 = 1$
2	d	$e \div 2 = 2$
3	b	$3 \cdot c = 3$
4	e	$f - 3 = 4$
5	a	$b + 2 = 5$
6	x	Treasure
7	f	$x + 1 = 7$

4. For *Part One,* make seven copies of the picture of the hole and write the numbers one through seven in the holes. Tape the pages in order across the bottom of a whiteboard or chalkboard. Place the chests in the chalk tray in front of the corresponding holes.

5. There are two treasure tracks pages for *Part Two*—one with chests and one with keys. The pages must be copied front to back so that the chests are on one side and the keys are on the other. Each row of clues (numbered one through seven) is a different treasure track.

6. Make enough copies of the treasure tracks pages so that each group can have one treasure track. After making the copies, cut the cards apart along the bold lines and fold each card along the dotted line so that the key is on the inside. Put each track into an envelope. When a group finishes one track, they can trade with another group that has a different track.

Procedure

Part One—Whole Class

1. If available, show the students the *Tracks1 Intro* animation.

2. Explain the scenario to the class and have a student come up to the number line of chests to act out the problem.

3. Have a second volunteer read the clue of the open chest while the student at the number lines acts out the solution. When the student decides which chest matches the clue, have him/her check on the back of the chest to verify that it has the same letter as in the clue. If the correct chest has been identified, have the student place the paper back on the chalk tray with the letter facing the class.

4. Discuss with the class how to record the clue and solution on the record page for the class tracks.

5. Continue to have the clues read, acted out, checked, and recorded until the treasure is found. The student volunteers can be changed between each chest, or when the student acting out the solution chooses a chest incorrectly.

6. Follow a similar procedure for each of the three class treasure tracks or until the class is proficient with the procedures.

7. Discuss with the class how they used the clues to find the next chest to verify that they understand the concepts of inverse operations and equality.

Part Two—Small Groups

1. Split the class into small groups and distribute a record page for the group tracks and an envelope with a track in it to each group. Instruct the groups to track down the treasure by following each clue and recording the clues and solutions. Tell students to begin with the numbered clue that has a picture of an open treasure chest on it.

2. As groups successfully record the tracks to the treasure, facilitate the exchange of tracks until every group has completed all four.

3. Have students practice solving one-step equations by completing *Practice Tracks*.

Connecting Learning

1. How do you undo taking forward steps or adding? [step backward, subtract]
2. How do you undo taking backward steps or subtracting? [step forward, add]
3. How do you undo multiplication? [division]
4. How do you undo division? [multiplication]
5. How do you undo any operation? [Use the opposite or inverse operation.]

Extension

Blank pages of chests and keys are included so that students can develop their own treasure tracks. They play the part of the pirate and write treasure on the inside of one of the chest pages and record the letter *x* on the key. They choose chests in sequence and record the clue on the inside describing how to get to the prior chest using the prior card's letter as the unknown variable (*x* for the first clue). They record the next letter on the back of the card and proceed. When students have made their tracks, they should start with the first clue and check that the clues bring them back to the treasure. Students exchange tracks and see if they can find the treasure.

Solutions

Practice Tracks

	x	*a*	*b*	*c*	*d*
Track 1	1	3	6	2	4
Track 2	7	3	1	4	6
Track 3	2	7	6	3	5
Track 4	6	3	2	4	7
Track 5	3	6	4	2	5
Track 6	5	7	4	2	6
Track 7	4	6	2	1	7

* Reprinted with permission from *Principles and Standards for School Mathematics*, 2000 by the National Council of Teachers of Mathematics. All rights reserved.

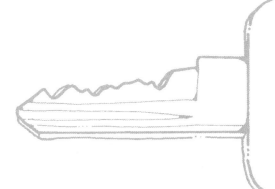

Key Question

How do you use the clue to find the treasure?

Learning Goals

Students will:

• recognize that working backwards through an instruction leads to the original condition, and

• use inverse operations to solve one-step equations.

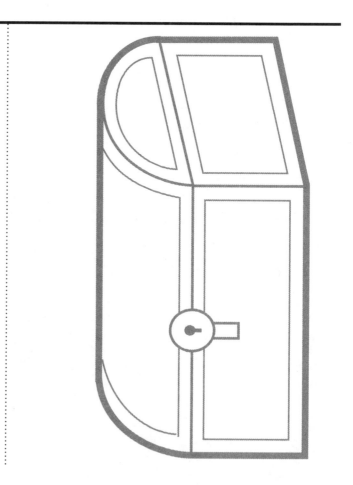

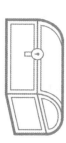

TRACKING TREASURE ONE-HOLE

TRACKING TREASURE ONE

Treasure Track One

x Clue f Clue e Clue d Clue c Clue b Clue a

Treasure Chest Chest Chest Chest Chest Chest Chest

Treasure Track Two

x Clue f Clue e Clue d Clue c Clue b Clue a

Treasure Chest Chest Chest Chest Chest Chest Chest

Treasure Track Three

x Clue f Clue e Clue d Clue c Clue b Clue a

Treasure Chest Chest Chest Chest Chest Chest Chest

TRACKING TREASURE ONE

GROUP TREASURE TRACKS—CHESTS
Part Two

A-1 c 1	A-2 d 2	A-3 b 3	A-4 f 4	A-5 a 5	A-6 e 6	A-7 x 7
B-1 c 1	B-2 e 2	B-3 x 3	B-4 d 4	B-5 f 5	B-6 b 6	B-7 a 7
C-1 x 1	C-2 d 2	C-3 f 3	C-4 a 4	C-5 e 5	C-6 c 6	C-7 b 7
D-1 a 1	D-2 c 2	D-3 b 3	D-4 e 4	D-5 x 5	D-6 c 6	D-7 f 7

Treasure (A-7)	$f + 2 = 6$ (A-6)	$b + 2 = 5$ (A-5)	$x - 3 = 4$ (A-4)	$3 \cdot c = 3$ (A-3)	$e \div 3 = 2$ (A-2)	$d - 1 = 1$ (A-1)
$b + 1 = 7$ (B-7)	$c + 5 = 6$ (B-6)	$x + 2 = 5$ (B-5)	$e \cdot 2 = 4$ (B-4)	Treasure (B-3)	$f - 3 = 2$ (B-2)	$d \div 4 = 1$ (B-1)
$c + 1 = 7$ (C-7)	$3 \cdot d = 6$ (C-6)	$f + 2 = 5$ (C-5)	$b - 3 = 4$ (C-4)	$3 \cdot x = 3$ (C-3)	$e - 3 = 2$ (C-2)	Treasure (C-1)
$x + 2 = 7$ (D-7)	$3 \cdot d = 6$ (D-6)	Treasure (D-5)	$f - 3 = 4$ (D-4)	$c \div 2 = 3$ (D-3)	$e \div 2 = 2$ (D-2)	$b - 2 = 1$ (D-1)

SOLVING EQUATIONS: A CONCEPTUAL APPROACH

TRACKING TREASURE ONE

GROUP RECORDS
Part Two

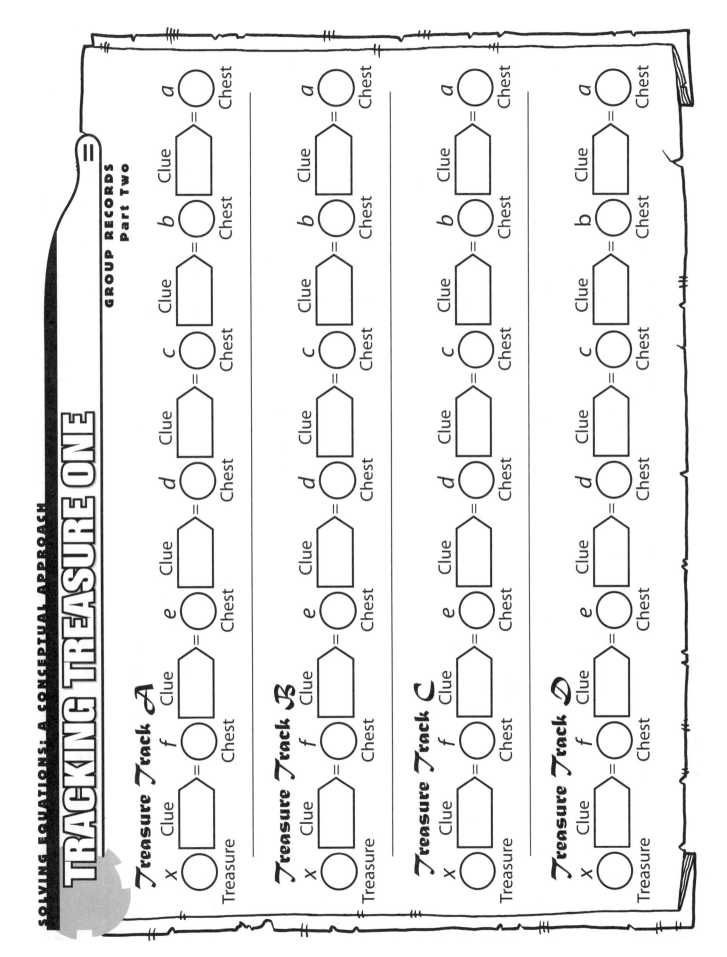

SOLVING EQUATIONS

45

© 2007 AIMS Education Foundation

TRACKING TREASURE ONE

Use the clues to work backwards and find what chest is marked by the **X** and has the treasure.

Track 1

x ◯ Treasure — Clue $x + 2$ = a ◯ Chest — Clue $a \cdot 2$ = b ◯ Chest — Clue $b \div 3$ = c ◯ Chest — Clue $c + 2$ = d ④ Chest

Track 2

x ◯ Treasure — Clue $x - 4$ = a ◯ Chest — Clue $a \div 3$ = b ◯ Chest — Clue $b \cdot 4$ = c ◯ Chest — Clue $c + 2$ = d ⑥ Chest

Track 3

x ◯ Treasure — Clue $x + 5$ = a ◯ Chest — Clue $a - 1$ = b ◯ Chest — Clue $b \div 2$ = c ◯ Chest — Clue $c + 2$ = d ⑤ Chest

Track 4

x ◯ Treasure — Clue $x \div 2$ = a ◯ Chest — Clue $a - 1$ = b ◯ Chest — Clue $b \cdot 2$ = c ◯ Chest — Clue $c + 3$ = d ⑦ Chest

Track 5

x ◯ Treasure — Clue $x \cdot 2$ = a ◯ Chest — Clue $a - 2$ = b ◯ Chest — Clue $b \div 2$ = c ◯ Chest — Clue $c + 3$ = d ⑤ Chest

Track 6

x ◯ Treasure — Clue $x + 2$ = a ◯ Chest — Clue $a - 3$ = b ◯ Chest — Clue $b \div 2$ = c ◯ Chest — Clue $c + 4$ = d ⑥ Chest

Track 7

x ◯ Treasure — Clue $x + 2$ = a ◯ Chest — Clue $a \div 3$ = b ◯ Chest — Clue $b - 1$ = c ◯ Chest — Clue $c \cdot 7$ = d ⑦ Chest

46

TRACKING TREASURE ONE

1	2	3	4	5	6	7
1	**2**	**3**	**4**	**5**	**6**	**7**

1	2	3	4	5	6	7
1	**2**	**3**	**4**	**5**	**6**	**7**

1	2	3	4	5	6	7
1	**2**	**3**	**4**	**5**	**6**	**7**

1	2	3	4	5	6	7
1	**2**	**3**	**4**	**5**	**6**	**7**

47

TRACKING TREASURE ONE

BLANK TREASURE KEYS
Extension

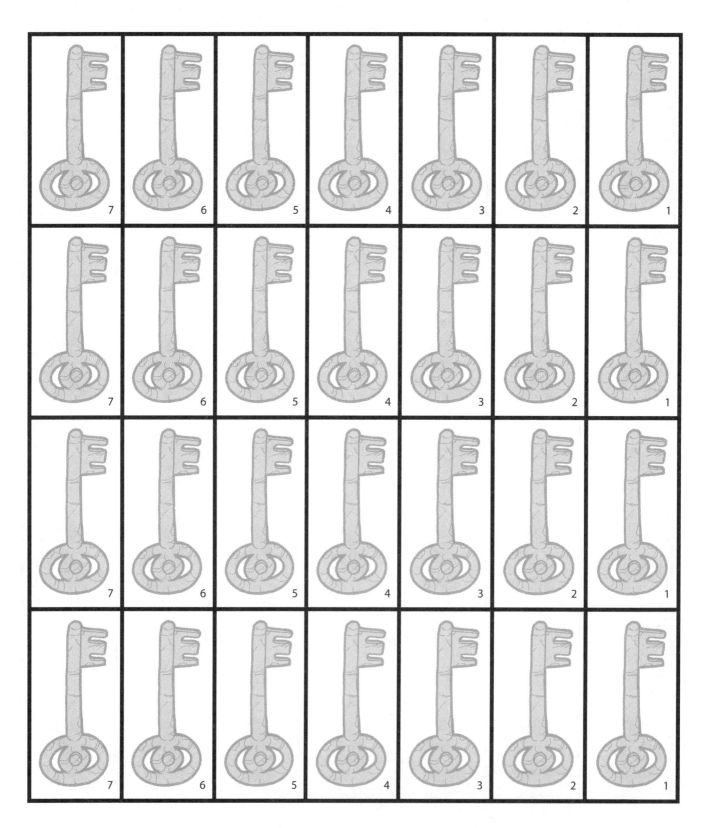

Connecting Learning

1. How do you undo taking forward steps or adding?

2. How do you undo taking backward steps or subtracting?

3. How do you undo multiplication?

4. How do you undo division?

5. How do you undo any operation?

BACKTRACKING ESP
Extraordinary Solution Prediction

Topic
Inverse operations

Key Question
How can you determine what a person chose as his or her starting number in an ESP problem from the person's ending number?

Learning Goals
Students will:
- recognize the relationship between the outcome of a procedure to its input, and
- become skilled at working backwards numerically through a multiple-step procedure using inverse operations.

Guiding Documents
Project 2061 Benchmarks
- *Mathematics is the study of many kinds of patterns, including numbers and shapes and operations on them. Sometimes patterns are studied because they help to explain how the world works or how to solve practical problems, sometimes because they are interesting in themselves.*
- *In using mathematics, choices have to be made about what operations will give the best results. Results should always be judged by whether they make sense and are useful.*
- *Add, subtract, multiply, and divide whole numbers mentally, on paper, and with a calculator.*
- *State the purpose of each step in a calculation.*

NCTM Standards 2000*
- *Identify and use relationships between operations, such as division as the inverse of multiplication, to solve problems*
- *Describe, extend, and make generalizations about geometric and numeric patterns*
- *Represent the idea of a variable as an unknown quantity using a letter or a symbol*
- *Express mathematical relationships using equations*

Math
Number
    Inverse operations
Algebra
    finding patterns
    solving equations

Integrated Processes
Observing
Comparing and contrasting
Generalizing
Applying

Materials
ESP Intro animation (see *Management 2*)
Student pages

Background Information
A strong understanding of the inverse nature of addition and subtraction and multiplication and division is required to solve equations at the algebraic level. This understanding of inverse operations can be gained at the very early stages of numeric computation.

There are many "mind reading" tricks that involve numbers. The spectator is asked to choose a number. Then he is asked to use that starting number in a series of simple computations. The mind reader determines the spectator's starting number (s) when told the ending number (e).

Consider the following trick procedure where seven has been chosen as the starting number.
- A. Choose a number. (7)
- B. Add five to your number. (7 + 5 = 12)
- C. Triple your sum. (12 · 3 = 36)
- D. Subtract three from the product. (36 – 3 = 33)
- E. Divide your answer by three. (33 ÷ 3 = 11)

With this procedure and a starting number of seven, the ending number is 11.

The mind reader, however, must start with the end number and tell the beginning number. There are several ways to do this. One way is to undo the steps by doing each step using the inverse operation (backtracking). Consider this method if the end result were eight.

Inverse Process
- E. Multiply your answer by three. (8 · 3 = 24)
- D. Add three to the product. (24 + 3 = 27)
- C. Divide by three. (27 ÷ 3 = 9)
- B. Subtract five from your number. (9 – 5 = 4)
- A. Starting number. (4)

By using the inverse operations, the mind reader could determine that when the ending number is eight, the starting number is four.

Although a mind reader could practice and get quick, it hardly appears to be magic. After doing just two tricks, you might notice that the ending number is always four bigger than the starting number. This pattern can be recorded in three different ways.

$$e = s + 4$$
$$s = e - 4$$
$$e - s = 4$$

Many students may recognize these equations as the addition fact families. The fact family for an ending number of 11 is:

$$11 = 7 + 4$$
$$7 = 11 - 4$$
$$11 - 4 = 7$$

The mind reader recognizes that for this particular problem, any of these equations will produce the desired result. The mind reader only needs to remember the equation that most quickly produces the starting number. The equation $s = e - 4$ produces the starting number simply by subtracting four from the number the spectator says was his ending number.

Management

1. The teacher instruction video *Part Four: Inverse Operations* is on the accompanying DVD. It is also available at the following URL: www.aimsedu.org/media/books/. It provides the rationale and suggestions for using this activity successfully in your classroom.

2. The animation *ESP Intro* is on the accompanying DVD and at the URL listed above. Make preparations in your classroom so students can view the animation. If viewing through a computer, a projector enhances the experience.

3. The motivational aspect to this activity lies in the magical nature of the presentation. Before beginning the lesson, you should be familiar with the solution equation for each trick and practice what magical flourishes are to be included in the presentation.

4. Remember, and remind the students, that a magician never reveals how a trick is done. The joy is in discovering for oneself a solution. Encourage the students to work the tricks forward and backward several times to find and verify the solution method. Those students who discover the trick can become mind readers.

5. Students will find the first four tricks relatively simple and may jump to the final solution quickly. Encourage them to work through the procedure forward and backward several times to confirm their solutions. The last two tricks involve both multiplication and addition in their solutions. Many students will have more difficulty finding an equation for these problems and will need to work through the procedure many times before recognizing a pattern. The next activity in the sequence (*Manipulating Extraordinary Solution Prediction*) will help students deal with these compound equations.

6. This activity is designed to develop algebraic thinking concepts of working backwards in solving equations. It is most appropriate for middle and upper elementary students. Teachers of pre-algebra and algebra classes may find it useful as an introduction to solving equations.

Procedure

1. Set the stage for the activity by verbally listing the procedure to the first trick while students calculate their ending numbers. Read the minds of several students by asking their ending numbers and telling them their starting numbers.

2. Distribute the student pages and have the students compute and record the outcome of each step of the procedure.

3. After students complete several trials of the trick, have them backtrack several samples of ending numbers to determine starting numbers.

4. Referring to the starting and ending numbers that have been calculated, have students generalize the relationship between the numbers and write it as an equation in the *Solution* area.

5. As a class, have students share and record the family of possible equations and how the equations are the mind reader's code.

6. Follow a similar sequence for each trick.

Connecting Learning

1. How do you undo something that has been done to a number? [use the inverse operation]

2. What patterns do you see in the relationship of the end number to the starting number? (See *Solutions*.)

3. How can you write the relationship of the ending number (e) to the starting number (s) as an equation? What equivalent equations can you write? (See *Solutions*.)

4. How can you use your equation to magically find the starting number in the magic trick? [substitute the ending number for (e) and calculate]

5. What patterns do you see in the numbers that were used to add, subtract, multiply and divide? [multiple operations disguise total of what is done, but common factors must be generated]

Extension

Encourage students to experiment developing their own procedures. Warn them it is not just a random selection for numbers and operations. They might want to study the tricks provided and see how there is a need to keep common multiples in the factors, sums, and divisors. Many students will develop solutions by trial and error. A blank record sheet is provided.

Solutions

	e $\longrightarrow$ s	Relationship	Equations
Trick One	4 $\longrightarrow$ 0 8 $\longrightarrow$ 4 11 $\longrightarrow$ 7	End number is four larger than the starting number.	$e = s + 4$ $s = e - 4$ $e - s = 4$
Trick Two	7 $\longrightarrow$ 4 11 $\longrightarrow$ 8 4 $\longrightarrow$ 1	End number is three larger than the starting number.	$e = s + 3$ $s = e - 3$ $e - s = 3$
Trick Three	16 $\longrightarrow$ 8 10 $\longrightarrow$ 5 0 $\longrightarrow$ 0	End number is two times larger than the starting number.	$e = 2 \cdot s$ $s = e \div 2$ $e \div s = 2$
Trick Four	12 $\longrightarrow$ 4 27 $\longrightarrow$ 9 15 $\longrightarrow$ 5	End number is three times larger than the starting number.	$e = 3 \cdot s$ $s = e \div 3$ $e \div s = 3$
Trick Five	13 $\longrightarrow$ 5 9 $\longrightarrow$ 3 21 $\longrightarrow$ 9	End number is two times the starting number plus three.	$e = 2s + 3$ $s = (e - 3) \div 2$
Trick Six	11 $\longrightarrow$ 2 23 $\longrightarrow$ 6 14 $\longrightarrow$ 3	End number is three times the starting number plus five.	$e = 3s + 5$ $s = (e - 5) \div 3$

BACKTRACKING ESP
Extraordinary Solution Prediction ≡

Key Question

How can you determine what a person chose as his or her starting number in an ESP problem from the person's ending number?

Learning Goals

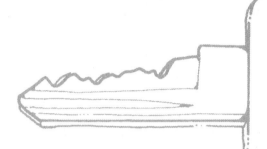

Students will:

- recognize the relationship between the outcome of a procedure to its input, and

- become skilled at working backwards numerically through a multiple-step procedure using inverse operations.

BACKTRACKING ESP
Extraordinary Solution Prediction

TRICKS ONE & TWO

TRACKING THE TRICK

START

END

Backtracking ESP - Trick One

A. Choose a number.

B. Add five to your number.

C. Triple the sum.

D. Subtract three from the product.

E. Divide your answer by three.

Solution:

START

END

4 **8** **11**

BACKTRACKING THE TRICK

TRACKING THE TRICK

START

END

Backtracking ESP - Trick Two

A. Choose a number.

B. Double your number.

C. Add six to your number.

D. Double your sum.

E. Divide your answer by four.

Solution:

START

END

7 **11** **4**

BACKTRACKING THE TRICK

BACKTRACKING ESP
Extraordinary Solution Prediction
TRICKS THREE & FOUR

TRACKING THE TRICK
START

END

Backtracking ESP - Trick Three
A. Choose a number.

B. Increase your number by five.

C. Multiply your sum by six.

D. Subtract 15.

E. Divide your answer by three.

F. Decrease the solution by five.

Solution:

START

END
16 **10** **0**

BACKTRACKING THE TRICK

TRACKING THE TRICK
START

END

Backtracking ESP - Trick Four
A. Choose a number.

B. Multiply your number by six.

C. Add 10 to the product.

D. Double your sum.

E. Subtract 20 from the product.

F. Divide the result by four.

Solution:

START

END
12 **27** **15**

BACKTRACKING THE TRICK

BACKTRACKING ESP
Extraordinary Solution Prediction
TRICKS FIVE & SIX

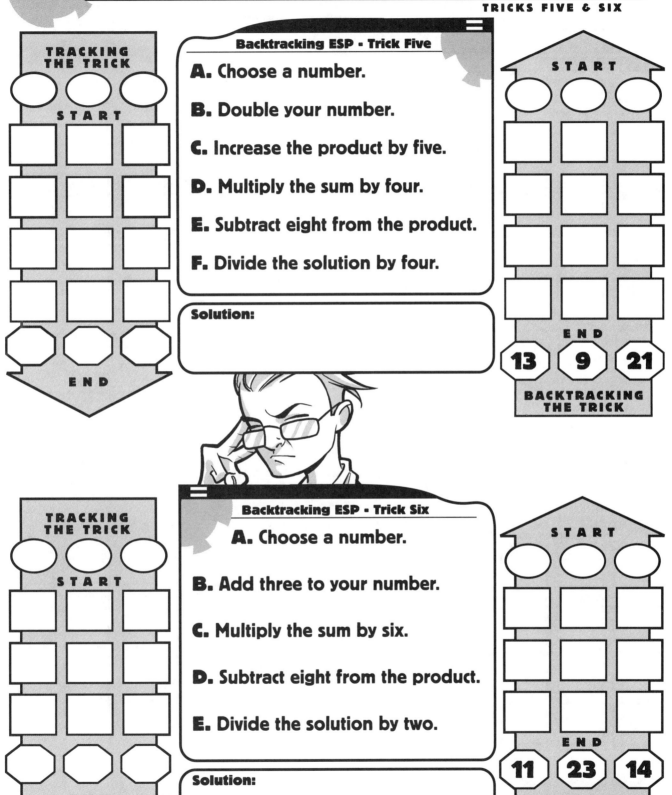

TRACKING THE TRICK

START

END

Backtracking ESP - Trick Five

A. Choose a number.

B. Double your number.

C. Increase the product by five.

D. Multiply the sum by four.

E. Subtract eight from the product.

F. Divide the solution by four.

Solution:

START

END

13 9 21

BACKTRACKING THE TRICK

TRACKING THE TRICK

START

END

Backtracking ESP - Trick Six

A. Choose a number.

B. Add three to your number.

C. Multiply the sum by six.

D. Subtract eight from the product.

E. Divide the solution by two.

Solution:

START

END

11 23 14

BACKTRACKING THE TRICK

BACKTRACKING ESP
Extraordinary Solution Prediction
EXTENSION

TRACKING THE TRICK

START

END

Backtracking ESP _____

A. _____

B. _____

C. _____

D. _____

E. _____

F. _____

Solution:

START

END

BACKTRACKING THE TRICK

TRACKING THE TRICK

START

END

Backtracking ESP _____

A. _____

B. _____

C. _____

D. _____

E. _____

F. _____

Solution:

START

END

BACKTRACKING THE TRICK

BACKTRACKING ESP Extraordinary Solution Prediction

Connecting Learning

1. How do you undo something that has been done to a number?

2. What patterns do you see in the relationship of the end number to the starting number?

3. How can you write the relationship of the ending number (e) to the starting number (s) as an equation? What equivalent equations can you write?

4. How can you use your equation to magically find the starting number in the magic trick?

5. What patterns do you see in the numbers that were used to add, subtract, multiply and divide?

MANIPULATING ESP
Extraordinary Solution Prediction

Topic
Solving equations

Key Question
How can you determine the solution to an ESP trick when you cannot work backwards?

Learning Goals
Students will:
- learn to translate a procedure of math operations into algebraic expressions;
- learn to use basic operations in algebraic form, including the use of distribution; and
- work backwards with compound algebraic expressions to solve equations.

Guiding Documents
Project 2061 Benchmarks
- *Mathematical ideas can be represented concretely, graphically, and symbolically.*
- *Numbers and shapes—and operations on them— help to describe and predict things about the world around us.*
- *Add, subtract, multiply, and divide whole numbers mentally, on paper, and with a calculator.*
- *State the purpose of each step in a calculation.*

NCTM Standards 2000*
- *Identify and use relationships between operations, such as division as the inverse of multiplication, to solve problems*
- *Understand and use properties of operations, such as the distributivity of multiplication over addition*
- *Represent the idea of a variable as an unknown quantity using a letter or a symbol*
- *Express mathematical relationships using equations*
- *Use symbolic algebra to represent situations and to solve problems, especially those that involve linear relationships*
- *Recognize and generate equivalent forms for simple algebraic expressions and solve linear equations*

Math
Number
    distributive property
Algebra
    finding patterns
    solving equations

Integrated Processes
Observing
Comparing and contrasting
Generalizing
Applying

Materials
ESP Intro animation (see *Management 2*)
Small cups, 6 per student
Counters (beans, pennies, paper clips), 20 per student
Student page

Background Information
There are a number of mind reading tricks that involve numbers. The participant is asked to choose a number. He or she in then asked to use that starting number in a series of simple computations. The mind reader's trick is to predict the end regardless of what number the participant starts with.

Consider the following trick procedure showing what happens when either seven or four is chosen as the starting number.

A. Choose a number. $(7)(4)$
B. Add three to your number. $(7 + 3 = 10)(4 + 3 = 7)$
C. Multiply the sum by six. $(10 \cdot 6 = 60)(7 \cdot 6 = 42)$
D. Divide by three. $(60 \div 3 = 20)(42 \div 3 = 14)$
E. Add four. $(20 + 4 = 24)(14 + 4 = 18)$
F. Take half of the number. $(24 \div 2 = 12)(18 \div 2 = 9)$
G. Subtract the original number. $(12 - 7 = 5)(9 - 4 = 5)$

With this procedure, no matter what number is chosen to start with, the ending number is always five. Knowing this, the mind reader can amaze the audience by telling them the final number is five without asking them.

How does this amazing trick work? The strategy of backtracking through the procedure cannot be used in this case. The last step is to subtract the original number, which is unknown. This means you cannot reverse the process by adding the original number.

At this point, one of the big ideas in algebra comes into play—the use of something to represent the unknown number. We call this a variable. Now we can use a variable in place of the starting number and work through the problem to see what happens. At a manipulative level, an object, such as a small cup, can be used to represent the variable. Any small counters, such as beans or pennies, can be used to represent the numbers that are added or subtracted.

58

Symbolically, letters are used as variables in algebra. Let (c), for cup, represent the starting number. Using the manipulatives and symbols, the procedure can be done again.

A. Choose a number. (a cup)(c)
B. Add three to your number. (a cup plus three objects)(c + 3)
C. Multiply the sum by six. (six cups plus 18 objects)(6c + 18)
D. Divide by three. (two cups plus six objects)(2c + 6)
E. Add four. (two cups plus 10 objects)(2c + 10)
F. Take half of the number. (a cup plus five objects) (c + 5)
G. Subtract the original number. (five objects)(5)

Using the manipulative or symbols allows one to see how the starting number or variable is removed from the problem leaving only a number. Students quite naturally use the distributive property at step C where the nature of the manipulative encourages them to multiply both the cups and the counters by six. Likewise, in step D, they factor out a three by dividing both the cups and the counters. If it is appropriate, this is an excellent time to discuss the distributive property and factors. The physical manipulation of the cups and counters requires that students use these properties even if they do not identify them. As students connect their symbolic representations with their physical operations, they will correctly apply the distributive property and factoring. This experience provides a strong physical memory that students can recall as they deal with only a symbolic representation in the future.

This method of using a variable and working through the procedure also allows students to develop expressions for more complicated ESP tricks. Consider the following procedure.

A. Choose a number. (a cup)(c)
B. Add five to your number. (a cup plus five counters)(c + 5)
C. Triple the sum. (three cups plus 15 counters) (3c + 15)
D. Subtract three from the product. (three cups plus 12 counters)(3c + 12)
E. Add your original number. (four cups plus 12 counters)(4c + 12)
F. Take half of the sum. (two cups plus six counters)(2c + 6)

By using the manipulative, students have developed the relationship between the ending and starting numbers. If students have developed a working understanding of the inverse nature of addition and subtraction and multiplication and division, they can now use the expression to solve for the starting number at an algebraic level.

In the example, (c) represents the starting number and the ending number is 2c + 6. If a spectator's ending number were 22, a simple equation exists: 2c + 6 = 22. To backtrack, the adding six is undone by subtracting six: 2c = 16. Now the multiplying by two is undone by dividing by two: c = 8. The mind reader can now say the starting number was eight.

Management

1. The teacher instruction video *Part Four: Inverse Operations* is on the accompanying DVD. It is also available at the following URL: www.aimse-du.org/media/books/. It provides the rationale and suggestions for using this activity successfully in your classroom.
2. The animation *ESP Intro* is on the accompanying DVD and at the URL listed above. Make preparations in your classroom so students can view the animation. If viewing through a computer, a projector enhances the experience.
3. The motivational aspect to this activity lies in the magical nature of the presentation. Before beginning the lesson, get familiar with the solution equation for each trick and practice what magical flourishes are to be included in the presentation.
4. This activity is designed to develop algebraic thinking concepts of solving equations. It provides a manipulative that bridges to symbolic representation. It is assumed students are comfortable at working backwards and are familiar with the concepts and methods developed in the prior activity, *Backtracking ESP*.
5. Cups are suggested for a manipulative representing a variable. Smaller cups or portion cups work very well. Likewise, any other object can be used as counters. Pennies are easily accessible and students automatically count them as units.

Procedure

1. If available, show the students the *ESP Intro* animation.
2. Set the stage for activity by verbally listing the procedure of *Trick One* to the students while they calculate their ending numbers. "Read their minds" by knowing that the outcome is five.
3. Encourage the students to consider backtracking so they will notice that the last step of subtracting the original number requires that they know the number that they are looking for.
4. Distribute the cups and counters. Have the students use the manipulatives to work through each step of the procedure, drawing a picture and writing the expression of the value at each step. The students may mimic you as it is modeled.
5. Verbally list the procedure of *Trick Two* to the students while they calculate their ending numbers. Magically know their starting numbers when given their ending number by using the equation $s = (e - 6) \div 2$.

6. Challenge the students to crack the mind-reading code. As students recognize they cannot numerically work the problem backward, have them use the manipulatives and make a pictorial and symbolic record.
7. Match students up with a partner and have each one use a new starting number and determine its corresponding ending number.
8. Have them use their magical solution expression with their partner's end number to work the equation backward to determine their partner's starting number.
9. Follow a similar sequence for each trick.

Connecting Learning

1. Why can't *Trick One* be solved by working backwards? [You need to know the original number, the one you are looking for.]
2. How are a cup and a letter like each other when you solve these tricks? [They both stand for a number you don't know, an unknown, a variable.]
3. When you get an expression that represents how the ending number is related to the starting number, how do you determine the beginning number? [backtrack, undo the expression]
4. What patterns do you see in the numbers that were used to add, subtract, multiply and divide? [Multiple operations disguise the total of what is done, but common factors must be generated.]

Extension

Encourage students to experiment developing their own procedures. Warn them that it is not just a random selection for numbers and operations. They might want to study the tricks provided and see how there is a need to keep common multiples in the factors, sums, and divisors. Students should be encouraged to use the manipulative to develop the symbolic form. A blank record sheet is provided. Students can exchange problems or they can be distributed to the class.

Solutions

Trick One

A. Choose a number.	c
B. Add three to your number.	$c + 3$
C. Multiply the sum by six.	$6c + 18$
D. Divide by three.	$2c + 6$
E. Add four.	$2c + 10$
F. Take half of the number.	$c + 5$
G. Subtract the original number.	5

Trick Two

A. Choose a number.	c
B. Add three to your number.	$c + 3$
C. Triple the sum.	$3c + 9$
D. Subtract three from the product.	$3c + 6$
E. Add your original number.	$4c + 6$
F. Take half of the sum.	$2c + 3$

Trick Three

A. Choose a number.	c
B. Add two to your number.	$c + 2$
C. Multiply the sum by six.	$6c + 12$
D. Subtract four from the product.	$6c + 8$
E. Divide by two.	$3c + 4$
F. Subtract the original number.	$2c + 4$

Trick Four

A. Choose a number.	c
B. Add three to your number.	$c + 3$
C. Multiply the sum by six.	$6c + 18$
D. Subtract six from the product.	$6c + 12$
E. Divide by six.	$c + 2$
F. Subtract the original number.	2

* Reprinted with permission from *Principles and Standards for School Mathematics*, 2000 by the National Council of Teachers of Mathematics. All rights reserved.

MANIPULATING ESP
Extraordinary Solution Prediction

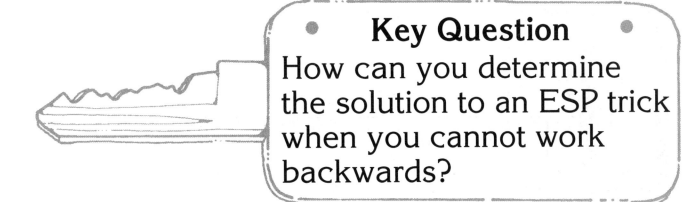

Key Question
How can you determine the solution to an ESP trick when you cannot work backwards?

Learning Goals

Students will:

- learn to translate a procedure of math operations into algebraic expressions;

- learn to use basic operations in algebraic form, including the use of distribution; and

- work backwards with compound algebraic expressions to solve equations.

MANIPULATING ESP

Extraordinary Solution Prediction

TRICK ONE

PROCEDURE	Picture of Cups & Counters	Symbol Description
A. Choose a number.	▱	C
B. Add three to your number.		
C. Multiply the sum by six.		
D. Divide by three.		
E. Add four.		
F. Take half of the number.		
G. Subtract the original number.		

Example:

▱ ▱ = ◯◯◯◯◯◯◯◯◯

▱ = ⁄⁄⁄⁄⁄ = 2c + 5

MANIPULATING ESP

Extraordinary Solution Prediction

TRICK TWO

PROCEDURE	Picture of Cups & Counters	Symbol Description
A. Choose a number.	⬜	c
B. Add three to your number.		
C. Triple the sum.		
D. Subtract three from the product.		
E. Add your original number.		
F. Take half of the sum.		

Example: ⬜ = 🎾🎾🎾🎾🎾 ⬜ ⬜ = 2c + 5

MANIPULATING ESP

Extraordinary Solution Prediction

TRICK THREE

PROCEDURE	Picture of Cups & Counters	Symbol Description
A. Choose a number.	▱	c
B. Add two to your number.		
C. Multiply the sum by six.		
D. Subtract four from the product.		
E. Divide by two.		
F. Subtract the original number.		

Example: ▱ ▱ = ⦾⦾⦾⦾⦾ = 2c + 5

64

MANIPULATING ESP

Extraordinary Solution Prediction

TRICK FOUR

PROCEDURE	Picture of Cups & Counters	Symbol Description
A. Choose a number.	▱	c
B. Add three to your number.		
C. Multiply the sum by six.		
D. Subtract six from the product.		
E. Divide by six.		
F. Subtract the original number.		

Example:

▱ = 2c + 5

MANIPULATING ESP

Extraordinary Solution Prediction

PROCEDURE	Picture of Cups & Counters	Symbol Description

66

MANIPULATING ESP Extraordinary Solution Prediction

Connecting Learning

1. Why can't *Trick One* be solved by working backwards?

2. How are a cup and a letter like each other when you solve these tricks?

3. When you get an expression that represents how the ending number is related to the starting number, how do you determine the beginning number?

4. What patterns do you see in the numbers that were used to add, subtract, multiply and divide?

© 2007 AIMS Education Foundation

ESP: EXTRAORDINARY SOLUTION PREDICTION

Topic
Solving equations

Key Question
How can you use algebraic symbols to determine how an ESP problem works?

Learning Goals
Students will:
* learn to translate a procedure of math operations into algebraic expressions,
* learn to simplify algebraic expressions using distribution and combining like terms, and
* work backwards with compound algebraic expressions to solve equations.

Guiding Documents
Project 2061 Benchmarks
* *Mathematical ideas can be represented concretely, graphically, and symbolically.*
* *Numbers and shapes—and operations on them— help to describe and predict things about the world around us.*
* *State the purpose of each step in a calculation.*

NCTM Standards 2000*
* *Identify and use relationships between operations, such as division as the inverse of multiplication, to solve problems*
* *Understand and use properties of operations, such as the distributivity of multiplication over addition*
* *Represent the idea of a variable as an unknown quantity using a letter or a symbol*
* *Express mathematical relationships using equations*
* *Use symbolic algebra to represent situations and to solve problems, especially those that involve linear relationships*
* *Recognize and generate equivalent forms for simple algebraic expressions and solve linear equations*

Math
Number
    operations
    distributive property
Algebra
    finding patterns
    solving equations

Integrated Processes
Observing
Comparing and contrasting

Generalizing
Applying

Materials
ESP Intro animation (see *Management 2*)
Student sheets
Calculators, optional

Background Information
In this "mind reading" display, the spectators are asked to choose a number. Then they are asked to use that starting number in a series of simple computations. The mind reader's power is that the end can be predicted, regardless of what number the spectator starts with, or the starting number can be predicted when given the ending number.

In an ESP problem, the numbers calculated often disguise what is actually going on. Translating and simplifying the operations at an algebraic level removes the disguise. It is obvious that if you increase a number by 10 and then remove 10, the result is the starting number. No one is amazed by *"Add 10, subtract 10—bingo, you have the starting number!"* But this obvious manipulation can be hidden in several steps, e.g., add two, multiply by five, subtract 10. This gives you five times the original number.

As students work through math problems algebraically, they begin to recognize methods of disguising what is being done. As a result, they can develop some very good "mind reading" problems of their own.

Consider the following ESP problem included in the *Extension* of this investigation. Be aware that the instructions were written for the year 2007 and need to be modified for other years by increasing the addition in step E. The answers given are for a 12-year-old who has already had his birthday this year.

Directions	Number	Algebra
Pick your favorite number from 0 to 10.	7	n
Multiply this number by 2.	14	$2n$
Add 5 to the product.	19	$2n + 5$
Multiply the sum by 50.	950	$100n + 250$
If you already had your birthday this year, add 1757. If you haven't had it, add 1756.	2707	$100n + 2007$
Subtract the four-digit year you were born.	712	$100n + 12$

68

You should get a 3-digit number. The digit in the hundreds place is the favorite number you choose. The remaining numbers in the tens and ones place are your age.

It is obvious if you take away the year you were born from the present year, you get your age. The present year of 2007 clearly shows up in the algebraic form. But 2007 is lost in the numbers when 250 (5 · 50) is added to 1757 along with the 100 times the original number. Getting the original number to the hundreds place is the result of multiplying it by two and then by 50.

As students work through these problems algebraically, they will recognize the power of algebra for solving problems and clarifying patterns.

The solution for the second extension problem is shown here for a 14-year-old with 47¢ in her pocket.

Directions	Number	Algebra
Enter your age in years.	14	a
Double your age.	28	$2a$
Add 5 to the product.	33	$2a + 5$
Multiply the sum by 50.	1650	$100a + 250$
Add the value, in cents, of the change in your pocket.	1697	$100a + 250 + c$
Subtract 365 from the sum.	1332	$100a - 115 + c$
Add 115 to the difference.	1447	$100a + c$
Divide the sum by 100.	14.47	$\dfrac{a + c}{100}$

The number to the left of the decimal point is your age, and the number to the right of the decimal point is the value of your change in dollars.

Management

1. The teacher instruction video *Part Four: Inverse Operations* is on the accompanying DVD. It is also available at the following URL: www.aimsedu.org/media/books/. It provides the rationale and suggestions for using this activity successfully in your classroom.

2. The animation *ESP Intro* is on the accompanying DVD and at the URL listed above. Make preparations in your classroom so students can view the animation. If viewing through a computer, a projector enhances the experience.

3. The motivational aspect to this activity lies in the mysterious nature of the presentation. Before beginning the lesson, you should be familiar with the solution equation for each problem and practice what mind-reading flourishes are to be included in the presentation.

4. If students master the algebraic modeling of the problem and working it backwards to solve the equation for the unknown starting number, make sure to have them work on the problems in the *Extension*. This will broaden their understanding of algebraic manipulation as well as let them see the power of using algebraic symbols to solve problems.

5. You may want to allow students to use calculators, especially on the *Extension* problems.

Procedure

1. If available, show the students the *ESP Intro* animation.

2. Set the stage for the activity by verbally listing the procedure of the first problem while students calculate their ending numbers. Ask a student to give you his or her ending number and practice your "ESP" by giving the starting number (to do this, subtract five from the ending number). Repeat this process with several students.

3. Distribute the first two student pages and have students compute and record the numeric outcome of each step of the procedure for the first problem.

4. Have students develop the algebraic expression for each step of the problem and encourage them to simplify at each step by using the distributive property and combining like terms.

5. Give the students several ending numbers and have them determine the starting numbers. If students have difficulty at this step, have them consider working backwards numerically to get started on the solution.

6. Have the students share the ways they determined the starting number. Some may choose to do it numerically, but they should be encouraged to develop algebraic skills.

7. Work through the other three problems in a similar manner.

8. As a class, have students consider all four problems and discuss what methods were used to disguise the mathematics that was going on during the problem.

9. Distribute the third student sheet. Ask each student to develop a procedure of his/her own for disguising what is being done mathematically. Have them record their steps on the student sheet and check to see that it works numerically and algebraically.

10. Allow students to practice their problems on each other and then exchange them so that each student checks someone else's problem to see how it works algebraically.

Connecting Learning

1. When you have the final expression and the ending number, how do you determine the starting number? [undo what has been done to the expression to get it back to the starting variable, do the same thing numerically to the ending number]
2. What methods did the developer of the ESP problems use to disguise what was being done mathematically? [split the process into several steps, e.g., an increase by 18 could be done by adding three and multiplying by six]
3. In what situations can't a problem be solved by working backwards with numbers? [when the original number is added or subtracted from the process]
4. What method(s) did you use when you made your own ESP problem?
5. How did these methods compare to those that your classmates used?
6. Which method(s) do you think are the most effective? Why?

Extension

Provide students with the *ESP Extension* pages. Have them try the problems numerically to see what the problems involve. Then have the students try to develop some more interesting ESP problems of their own. *Extension Number One* needs to be adjusted every year. Before copying the page for students, write the correct numbers for each year in the three appropriate blanks.

		(Year Used)
Blank One	Blank Two	Blank Three
17<u>57</u>	17<u>56</u>	20<u>07</u>
17<u>58</u>	17<u>57</u>	20<u>08</u>
17<u>59</u>	17<u>58</u>	20<u>09</u>
17<u>60</u>	17<u>59</u>	20<u>10</u>
17<u>61</u>	17<u>60</u>	20<u>11</u>

Solutions

ESP One: $n + 5$
ESP Two: $2n + 1$
ESP Three: 10
ESP Four: n

ESP: EXTRAORDINARY SOLUTION PREDICTION

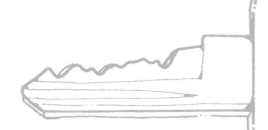

Key Question

How can you use algebraic symbols to determine how an ESP problem works?

Learning Goals

Students will:

- learn to translate a procedure of math operations into algebraic expressions,

- learn to simplify algebraic expressions using distribution and combining like terms, and

- work backwards with compound algebraic expressions to solve equations.

ESP: EXTRAORDINARY SOLUTION PREDICTION

PREDICTIONS ONE & TWO

Extraordinary Solution Prediction One

Directions	Number	Algebraic Expression
Choose a number.		
Add six to your number.		
Triple the sum.		
Decrease your product by three.		
Divide the difference by three.		

Extraordinary Solution Prediction Two

Directions	Number	Algebraic Expression
Choose a number.		
Add six to your number.		
Multiply the sum by three.		
Add the original number.		
Add 12 to the sum.		
Divide the sum by two.		
Subtract 14.		

ESP: EXTRAORDINARY SOLUTION PREDICTION

Extraordinary Solution Prediction Three

Directions	Number	Algebraic Expression
Choose a number.		
Add three to your number.		
Multiply the sum by four.		
Divide the product by two.		
Add 14.		
Take half the sum.		
Subtract the original number.		

Extraordinary Solution Prediction Four

Directions	Number	Algebraic Expression
Choose a number.		
Increase your number by five.		
Multiply the sum by five.		
Subtract 10 from the product.		
Divide the total by five.		
Subtract three.		

ESP: EXTRAORDINARY SOLUTION PREDICTION

Directions	Number	Algebraic Expression

Your Extraordinary Solution Prediction

ESP: EXTRAORDINARY SOLUTION PREDICTION

Extraordinary Solution Prediction Calculation		
Directions	**Number**	**Algebraic Expression**
Pick your favorite number between zero and 10.		
Multiply this number by two.		
Add five to the product.		
Multiply the sum by 50.		
If you already had your birthday this year, add _____. If you haven't had it yet, add _____.		
Subtract the four-digit year you were born.		

You should have a three-digit number. The digit in the hundreds place is the favorite number you chose. The remaining numbers in the tens and ones places are your age.

Use algebra symbols and expressions to see how this problem works.

This set of directions only works for the year _____ . How can you modify the directions to work for another year? Show your work.

75

ESP: EXTRAORDINARY SOLUTION PREDICTION

Extraordinary Solution Prediction Calculation

Directions	Number	Algebraic Expression
Enter your age in years.		
Double your age.		
Add five to the product.		
Multiply the sum by 50.		
Add the value, in cents, of the change in your pocket. If you have more than a dollar, use only the last two digits of the number of cents. (For example, if you have $2.43, use 43.)		
Subtract 365 from the product.		
Add 115 to the difference.		
Divide the sum by 100.		

The number to the left of the decimal point is your age, and the number ot the right of the decimal point is the value of your change.

Use algebra symbols and expressions to see how this problem works. Try using two variables—one for age (a), and one for cents (c).

ESP: EXTRAORDINARY SOLUTION PREDICTION

Connecting Learning

1. When you have the final expression and the ending number, how do you determine the starting number?

2. What methods did the developer of the ESP problems use to disguise what was being done mathematically?

3. In what situations can't a problem be solved by working backwards with numbers?

4. What method(s) did you use when you made your own ESP problem?

5. How did these methods compare to those that your classmates used?

6. Which method(s) do you think are the most effective? Why?

EQUALITY IN THE BALANCE

Topic
Solving equations

Key Question
How can you determine how many pennies are in a packet while keeping the balance level?

Learning Goals
Students will:
- learn that by subtracting equal amounts from both sides of a balance, equilibrium is maintained;
- learn that by dividing the contents of both sides of a balance by the same amount, equilibrium is maintained;
- model what is done on a balance in equations; and
- generalize their experiences with a balance in solving equations.

Guiding Documents
Project 2061 Benchmarks
- *An equation containing a variable may be true for just one value of the variable.*
- *Mathematical statements can be used to describe how one quantity changes when another changes. Rates of change can be computed from magnitudes and vice versa.*
- *The operations + and – are inverses of each other— one undoes what the other does; likewise x and ÷.*

NCTM Standards 2000*
- *Develop an initial conceptual understanding of different uses of variables*
- *Use symbolic algebra to represent situations and to solve problems, especially those that involve linear relationships*
- *Recognize and generate equivalent forms for simple algebraic expressions and solve linear equations*

Math
Algebra
    variables
    solving equations
        one-step equations
        multi-step equations

Integrated Processes
Observing
Comparing and contrasting
Generalizing

Materials
For each group:
    100 pennies (post 1983)
    5 sheets #20 or #24 paper
      (different color for each group)
    school balance (see *Management 2*)
    student pages

Background Information
The two big ideas in understanding how to solve equations are the concepts of inverse operations and maintaining equalities.

Using a balance as a model of equations emphasizes maintaining equalities. To keep a balance level, when something is removed or subtracted from one side, an equal amount needs to be removed from the other side. If multiple packets are on one side, they must be split up or divided so one packet is by itself on the balance. To maintain the equilibrium, the pennies on the other side must be split into the same number of equal groups leaving one group on the balance. The focus of this investigation is formally called the *properties of equality*. In terms of a level balance, when both sides are added to, subtracted from, or multiplied or divided by equal amounts, the balance stays level, or in equilibrium. In algebraic terms, when both expressions, or sides, of an equality or equation are changed or transformed by the same operation with equal quantities, the equality is maintained.

The object of the investigation is to determine how many pennies balance a packet filled with pennies. To do this, one needs to get a single packet balanced by pennies. The same physical operations required to do this on the balance are modeled in solving an equation. Consider a level balance where one side has four packets and three pennies and the other side has two packets and 15 pennies. The equation would be written.

$$4p + 3 = 2p + 15$$

(In algebra an unknown is often written as x or y. The variable in this case is p to provide meaning. When moving to abstract algebra, some attention will be need to be focused on the use of multiple letters for the unknown variable.) In order to get rid of the pennies on the left side, one would remove three pennies from both sides.

$$\begin{array}{rl} 4p + 3 &= 2p + 15 \\ \underline{-3} & \quad \underline{-3} \\ 4p &= 2p + 12 \end{array}$$

To get packets only on one side, one would remove two packets from both sides.

$$4p = 2p + 12$$
$$\underline{-2p \quad -2p}$$
$$2p = \qquad 12$$

Since only the weight of one packet is wanted, both sides would be split in two leaving one set on the balance.

$$\frac{2p}{2} = \frac{12}{2}$$
$$p = 6$$

Each of the packets has the same mass as six pennies.

In order to ensure that all students move to the symbolic level of solving equations, it is imperative that students record their physical actions in symbolic form. Students can quite intuitively move through the physical operations with the balance, though students initially may take single pennies or packets from both sides of the balance until they become more familiar with the process. Then they will remove the two or three that are required in one step. As students perform each physical act, they need to record what they did in symbols. As students build the conceptual understanding of why they are doing things, they will relate that understanding to the symbolic record. The students will progress to the point that they will translate equations into the balance model and think and act on symbols as they would the physical objects. With repetition, the students will internalize the routine of the repeated process and begin to abstractly manipulate the symbols without reference to the physical model. Since students have developed conceptual understanding when they forget the manipulations, they can go back to their memory of the model and recreate the routine.

Management

1. The teacher instruction video *Part Three: Equalities* is on the accompanying DVD. It is also available at the following URL: www.aimsedu.org/media/books/. It provides the rationale and suggestions for using this activity successfully in your classroom.
2. This investigation uses paper packets filled with pennies. These need to be prepared before doing the activity (see *Penny Packet Construction*). One set consists of five packets, each filled with the same number of pennies. Nine sets need to be made—each containing a different number of pennies (from one to nine). To distinguish the sets from one another, multiple colors of paper can be used. If only white paper is available, the packets can be identified with letters. Put the five identical packets from one set and approximately 50 loose pennies in a container (cup or plastic bag) so they can easily be exchanged between groups.

3. If school balances are not available, alternative balances can be made by following the instructions on the *Alternate Balance Construction* page.
4. This investigation is designed to be done in stages as understanding develops and should progress at a pace appropriate to student learning. The first stage is single-step solutions with both subtraction and division. The second is two-step solutions with the packets of unknown weight on only one side of the balance. The third stage is multi-step solutions with unknowns on both sides of the balance. The student pages for each stage encourage the movement from conceptual understanding to abstract routine. The first pages are completed with the balance to develop the conceptual understanding and to relate the physical motions to symbolic notation. The third page at each stage has a picture of the initial set-up of the balance and reinforces students' conceptual understanding by encouraging them to think of the process in the physical setting while recording what they are thinking of doing with symbolic equations. The final page presents the situations in symbolic notation and although most students are conceptualizing the process in physical terms, they record in only in symbolic. The final step is to present students with equations with no context and ask them to solve them using what routines they have developed. The pace at which students progress though these stages varies. If extra problems are required, you or students can generate some that are similar to those given.

Procedure

Introduction
1. In front of the class, put three packets and five pennies on the left side of a balance and two packets (from the same set) and enough pennies to level the balance on the right side of the balance. Have the students write the equation of what is in the balance. ($3p + 5 = 2p +$ ___)
2. Ask how they could remove pennies from the balance and keep it level. Have a student come up and demonstrate taking the same amount of pennies from each side of the balance to make it remain level.
3. Next, ask how packets can be removed from the balance while keeping it level. Have a student come up and demonstrate that by taking the same number of packets from each side of the balance, it remains level.

Developing Understanding
1. Distribute a balance, a set of penny packets, and the appropriate student pages to each group.
2. For each stage of development, (pages 1a, 1b, 2a, 2b, 3a, 3b) have students fill the balance as

shown in the drawing and level the balance by adding pennies to the noted side.

3. Ask students to determine the steps required to get a single packet to balance only pennies while keeping the balance level. Have the students try their ideas out on the balance and, when correct, record them on the record sheets as operations and equations. (Initially you may need to give some guidance on the symbolic representation, but this should be reduced as students make progress.)

4. As students complete each page, have them discuss and generalize what steps were followed in each of the situations.

Reinforcing Understanding

1. Encourage students to move to symbolic records by having them translate the picture of the balances on the record page (1c, 2c, 3c) to an equation. Then have them determine the pennies needed to balance a packet by referring to the balance situation and their generalizations from the development pages. They should record their steps in symbols that change the equations.

2. Have students complete the last record page (1d, 2d, 3d) by making a sketch of the original situation. Have the students determine the penny-weight of the packet, showing the steps required. They can refer to their sketches to make sense of the problem if they have difficulty.

Connecting Learning

1. How do you remove pennies or packets from a balance and keep it level? [Take the same number of pennies or packets from each side.]

2. What symbol do you use show the combinations of packets and pennies on the same side of the balance? [addition]

3. How do you show removing something with symbols? [Minus what you are taking away.]

4. If you have a pile of pennies level with a number of packets, how do you determine how many pennies it takes to balance each packet? [Divide the pennies into the same number of groups as the number of packets.]

5. If there are pennies and packets on the same side, what do you do to get packets alone? [Take away the pennies from the packet side and an equal number of pennies from the opposite side.]

6. When there are packets and pennies on both sides of the balance, what do you need to do to determine how many pennies balance a packet? [Get only packets on one side and pennies on the other.]

Extension

Have students complete problems of solving equations from their textbooks to make sure transfer of understanding takes place.

Solutions

Part One—C

1. $p + 4 = 12$
   $p = 8$
2. $2p = 12$
   $p = 6$
3. $p + 5 = 15$
   $p = 10$
4. $4p = 12$
   $p = 3$
5. $p + 2 = 9$
   $p = 7$
6. $5p = 25$
   $p = 5$
7. $p + 5 = 8$
   $p = 3$
8. $3p = 21$
   $p = 7$

Part One—D

1. $p + 3 = 9$
   $p = 6$
2. $3p = 12$
   $p = 4$
3. $p + 7 = 16$
   $p = 9$
4. $4p = 16$
   $p = 4$
5. $2p = 16$
   $p = 8$
6. $p + 2 = 13$
   $p = 11$
7. $p + 5 = 13$
   $p = 8$
8. $p + 6 = 9$
   $p = 3$
9. $7p = 21$
   $p = 3$
10. $5p = 30$
    $p = 6$

Part Two—C

1. $2p + 5 = 11$
   $2p = 6$
   $p = 3$
2. $3p = 2p + 7$
   $p = 7$
3. $3p + 3 = 15$
   $3p = 12$
   $p = 4$
4. $2p + 6 = 4p$
   $6 = 2p$
   $3 = p$
5. $5p + 1 = 11$
   $5p = 10$
   $p = 2$
6. $5p = 1p + 16$
   $4p = 16$
   $p = 4$
7. $15 = 4p + 3$
   $12 = 4p$
   $3 = p$
8. $4p + 8 = 6p$
   $8 = 2p$
   $4 = p$

Part Two—D

1. $4p + 3 = 11$
   $4p = 8$
   $p = 2$
2. $4p = 3p + 8$
   $p = 8$
3. $7p + 4 = 18$
   $7p = 14$
   $p = 2$
4. $5p = 2p + 15$
   $3p = 15$
   $p = 5$
5. $p + 8 = 3p$
   $8 = 2p$
   $4 = p$
6. $21 = 5p + 6$
   $15 = 5p$
   $3 = p$
7. $3p + 7 = 22$
   $3p = 15$
   $p = 5$
8. $17 = 2p + 3$
   $14 = 2p$
   $7 = p$
9. $6p = 3p + 18$
   $3p = 18$
   $p = 6$
10. $3p + 14 = 5p$
    $14 = 2p$
    $7 = p$

Part Three—C

1. $3p + 4 = 2p + 10$
   $p = 6$
2. $2p + 12 = 4p + 2$
   $10 = 2p$
   $5 = p$
3. $5p + 4 = 6p + 1$
   $3 = p$
4. $7p + 6 = 3p + 14$
   $4p = 8$
   $p = 2$
5. $5p + 1 = 2p + 16$
   $3p = 15$
   $p = 5$
6. $p + 15 = 4p + 3$
   $12 = 3p$
   $4 = p$
7. $3p + 11 = 4p + 3$
   $8 = p$
8. $6p + 5 = 15 + 4p$
   $2p = 10$
   $p = 5$

Part Three—D

1. $3p + 2 = p + 12$
   $2p = 10$
   $p = 5$
2. $5p + 4 = 3p + 18$
   $2p = 14$
   $p = 7$
3. $2p + 13 = 1 + 6p$
   $12 = 4p$
   $3 = p$
4. $2 + 7p = 4p + 11$
   $3p = 9$
   $p = 3$
5. $8p + 1 = 6p + 15$
   $2p = 14$
   $p = 7$
6. $p + 18 = 2 + 5p$
   $16 = 4p$
   $4 = p$
7. $5p + 19 = 7p + 1$
   $18 = 2p$
   $9 = p$
8. $3 + 8p = 23 + 4p$
   $4p = 20$
   $p = 5$
9. $3p + 21 = 6p + 3$
   $18 = 3p$
   $6 = p$
10. $8p + 1 = 5p + 16$
    $3p = 15$
    $p = 5$

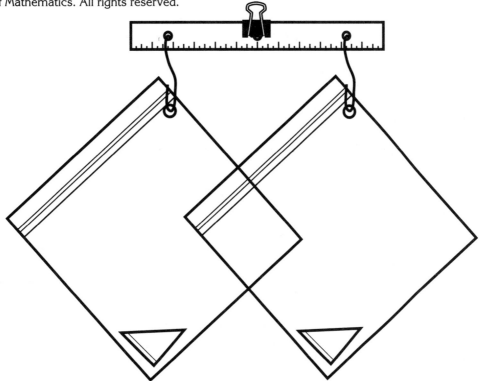

EQUALITY IN THE BALANCE

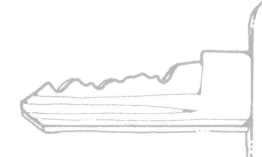

Key Question

How can you determine how many pennies are in a packet while keeping the balance level?

Learning Goals

Students will:

- learn that by subtracting equal amounts from both sides of a balance, equilibrium is maintained;

- learn that by dividing the contents of both sides of a balance by the same amount, equilibrium is maintained;

- model what is done on a balance in equations; and

- generalize their experiences with a balance in solving equations.

EQUALITY IN THE BALANCE

Penny Packet Construction

The paper from which each packet is made must have the same weight as a penny. The paper must be carefully cut before making the packets.

- For standard 20-lb copy paper, cut into strips that are 6 ⅛″ by 8 ½″.
- For 24-lb copy paper, cut into strips that are 5 ¼″ by 8 ½″.

To fold a packet:

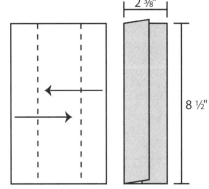

1. Begin with a single sheet of paper cut to the correct dimensions. Fold the sides of the paper in so that they overlap. The resulting paper should be about 2 ⅜″ (6 cm) wide. (This width is important for folding success.)

2. Fold the bottom edge up to meet the left side of the paper.

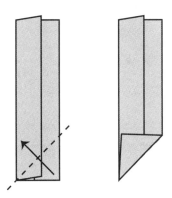

3. Drop the correct number of pennies into the pocket formed by the folded paper.

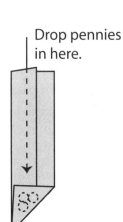

Drop pennies in here.

4. Using a flag fold, fold the paper up until there is only a small tab left.

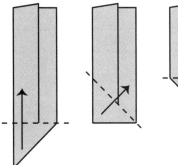 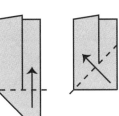

5. Fold down the top right corner of the tab. Tuck the tab into the pocket created by the folds in the previous step.

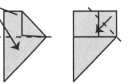

EQUALITY IN THE BALANCE

Alternate Balance Construction

Materials:
- Ruler with holes for 3-ring binder
- 1 medium binder clip
- 2 paper clips
- 2 identical plastic sandwich bags

Construction:
1. Fasten the binder clip on one edge of the ruler at the center. Fold back the wire handles so a pencil can be inserted through them. This is the fulcrum from which the balance hangs.

2. Unfold the paper clips into hooks and hang one from each of the outside holes of the ruler.

3. Punch holes in the corner of the two plastic bags and hang one from each of the paper clip hooks.

4. Adjust the position of the binder clip until the balance hangs level.

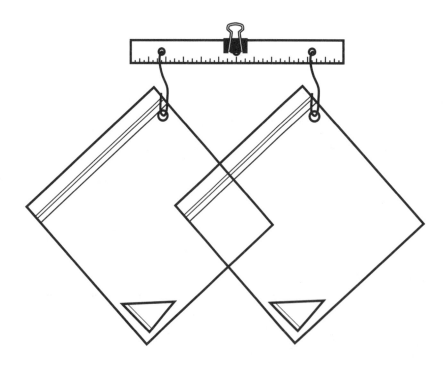

84

EQUALITY IN THE BALANCE

1. Put the number of packets and pennies shown in the picture on the left side of the balance. Then put pennies on the right side until the balance is level. Complete the picture and the equation to describe the situation.

2. Decide what you need to do to keep the balance level but get the packet by itself. Then try your plan out and see if it works.

3. If your plan works, show what you did mathematically using the equation.

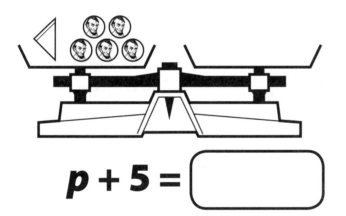

$$p + 5 = \boxed{}$$

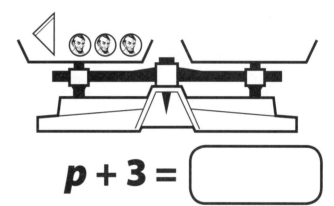

$$p + 3 = \boxed{}$$

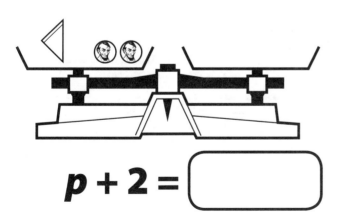

$$p + 2 = \boxed{}$$

$$p + 4 = \boxed{}$$

EQUALITY IN THE BALANCE

1. Put the number of packets shown in the picture on the left side of the balance. Then put pennies on the right side until the balance is level. Complete the picture and the equation to describe the situation.

2. Decide what you need to do to keep the balance level but get a single packet by itself. Then try your plan out and see if it works.

3. If your plan works, show what you did mathematically using the equation.

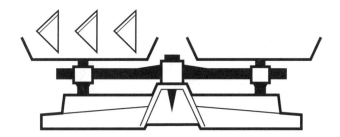

3p =

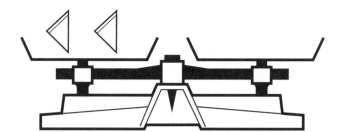

2p =

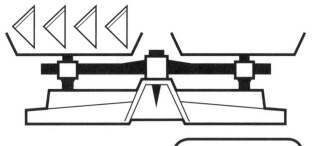

4p =

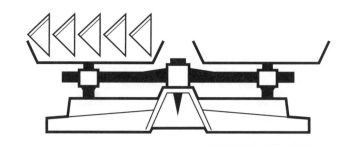

5p =

86

EQUALITY IN THE BALANCE

Translate each picture into an equation and then figure out how many pennies it would take to balance a packet. Show how to do it with an equation.

①

②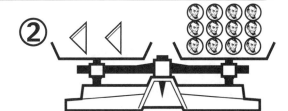

③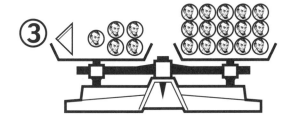

④

⑤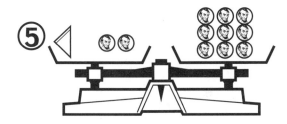

⑥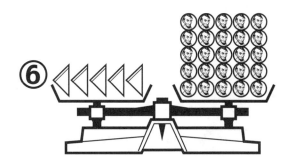

⑦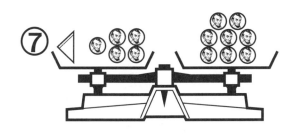

⑧

　　87

EQUALITY IN THE BALANCE

Make a picture from each equation and then figure out how many pennies it would take to balance a packet. Show how to do it with the equation.

①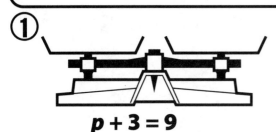

$p + 3 = 9$

②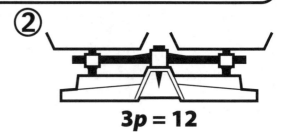

$3p = 12$

③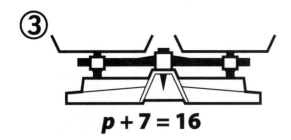

$p + 7 = 16$

④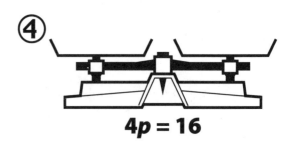

$4p = 16$

⑤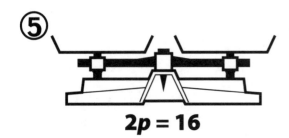

$2p = 16$

⑥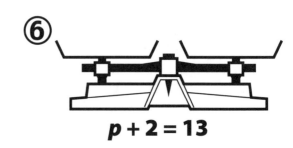

$p + 2 = 13$

⑦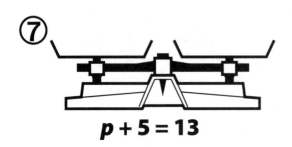

$p + 5 = 13$

⑧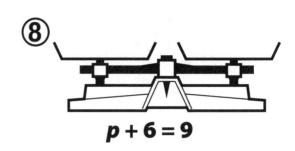

$p + 6 = 9$

⑨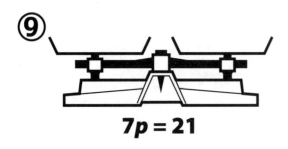

$7p = 21$

⑩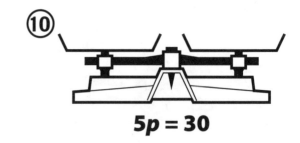

$5p = 30$

EQUALITY IN THE BALANCE

1. Put the number of packets and pennies shown in the picture on one side of the balance. Then put pennies on the opposite side until the balance is level. Complete the picture and make an equation to describe the situation.

2. Decide what you need to do to keep the balance level but get a single packet by itself. Then try your plan out and see if it works.

3. If your plan works, show what you did mathematically using the equation.

$3p + 2 =$

$2p + 4 =$

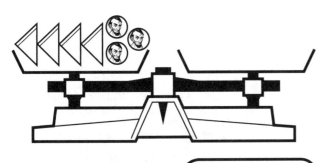

$4p + 3 =$

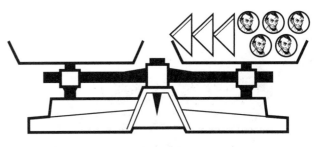

$= 3p + 5$

EQUALITY IN THE BALANCE

1. Put the number of packets shown in the picture on the balance. Then put pennies on the higher side until the balance is level. Complete the picture and the equation to describe the situation.

2. Decide what you need to do to keep the balance level but get a single packet by itself. Then try your plan out and see if it works.

3. If your plan works, show what you did mathematically using the equation.

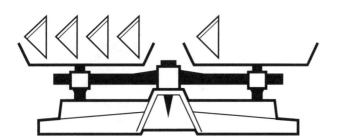

$$4p = 1p + \boxed{}$$

$$3p = 2p + \boxed{}$$

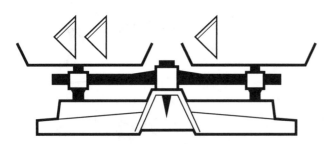

$$2p = 1p + \boxed{}$$

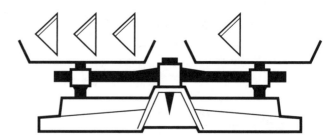

$$3p = 1p + \boxed{}$$

EQUALITY IN THE BALANCE

PART TWO · C

Translate each picture into an equation and then figure out how many pennies it would take to balance a packet. Show how to do it with an equation.

①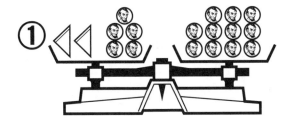

②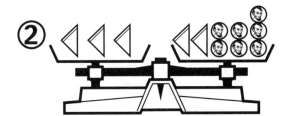

③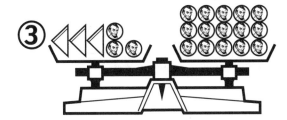

④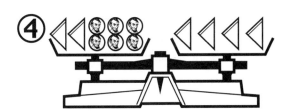

⑤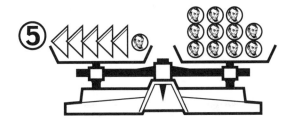

⑥

⑦

⑧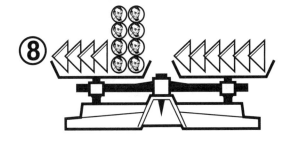

EQUALITY IN THE BALANCE

PART TWO · D

Make a picture from each equation and then figure out how many pennies it would take to balance a packet. Show how to do it using the equation.

①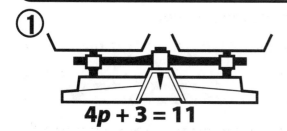

$$4p + 3 = 11$$

②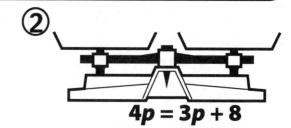

$$4p = 3p + 8$$

③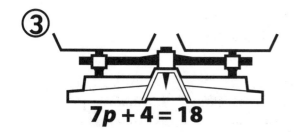

$$7p + 4 = 18$$

④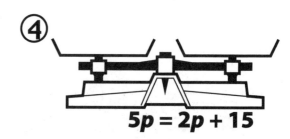

$$5p = 2p + 15$$

⑤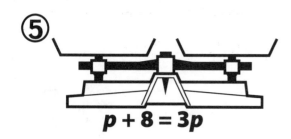

$$p + 8 = 3p$$

⑥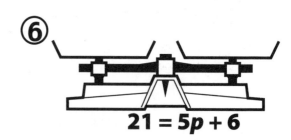

$$21 = 5p + 6$$

⑦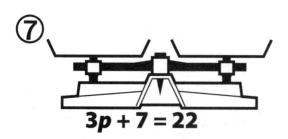

$$3p + 7 = 22$$

⑧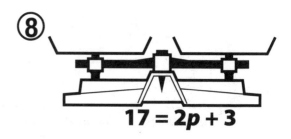

$$17 = 2p + 3$$

⑨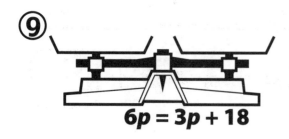

$$6p = 3p + 18$$

⑩

$$3p + 14 = 5p$$

EQUALITY IN THE BALANCE

1. Put the number of packets and pennies shown in the picture on the balance. Then put pennies on the higher side until the balance is level. Complete the picture and the equation to describe the situation.

2. Decide what you need to do to keep the balance level but get a single packet by itself. Then try your plan out and see if it works.

3. If your plan works, show what you did mathematically using the equation.

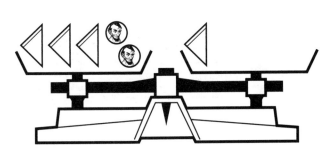

$$3p + 2 = p + \boxed{}$$

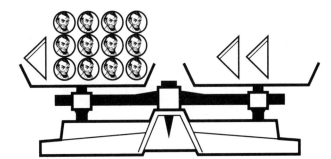

$$1p + 12 = 2p + \boxed{}$$

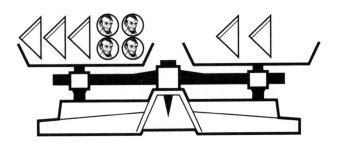

$$3p + 4 = 2p + \boxed{}$$

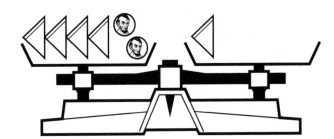

$$4p + 2 = p + \boxed{}$$

EQUALITY IN THE BALANCE

1. Put the number of packets and pennies shown in the picture on the balance. Then put pennies on the higher side until the balance is level. Complete the picture and the equation to describe the situation.

2. Decide what you need to do to keep the balance level but get a single packet by itself. Then try your plan out and see if it works.

3. If your plan works, show what you did mathematically using the equation.

$$2p + 2 = p + \boxed{}$$

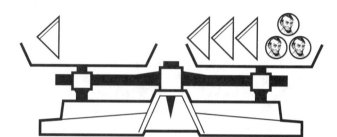

$$p + \boxed{} = 3p + 3$$

$$2p + 14 = 3p + \boxed{}$$

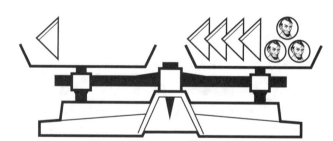

$$p + \boxed{} = 4p + 3$$

EQUALITY IN THE BALANCE

PART THREE · C

Translate each picture into an equation and then figure out how many pennies it would take to balance a packet. Show how to do it with an equation.

①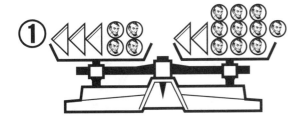

②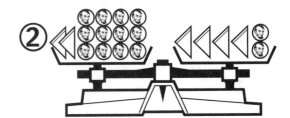

③

④

⑤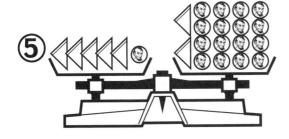

⑥

⑦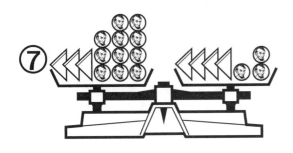

⑧

95

EQUALITY IN THE BALANCE

PART THREE · D

Make a picture from each equation and then figure out how many pennies it would take to balance a packet. Show how to do it with the equation.

①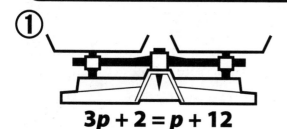

$$3p + 2 = p + 12$$

②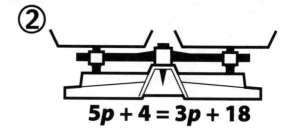

$$5p + 4 = 3p + 18$$

③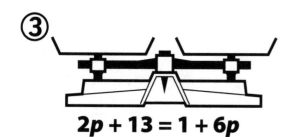

$$2p + 13 = 1 + 6p$$

④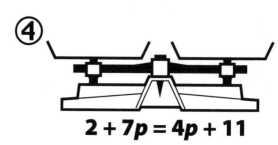

$$2 + 7p = 4p + 11$$

⑤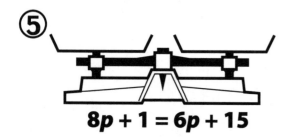

$$8p + 1 = 6p + 15$$

⑥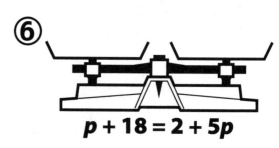

$$p + 18 = 2 + 5p$$

⑦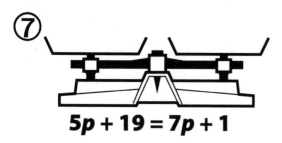

$$5p + 19 = 7p + 1$$

⑧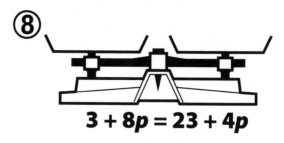

$$3 + 8p = 23 + 4p$$

⑨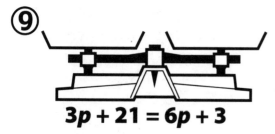

$$3p + 21 = 6p + 3$$

⑩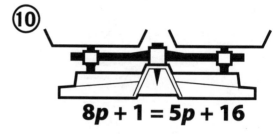

$$8p + 1 = 5p + 16$$

96

EQUALITY IN THE BALANCE

Connecting Learning

1. How do you remove pennies or packets from a balance and keep it level?

2. What symbol do you use show the combinations of packets and pennies on the same side of the balance?

3. How do you show removing something with symbols?

4. If you have a pile of pennies level with a number of packets, how do you determine how many pennies it takes to balance each packet?

5. If there are pennies and packets on the same side, what do you do to get packets alone?

6. When there are packets and pennies on both sides of the balance, what do you need to do to determine how many pennies balance a packet?

WHAT'S IN A CASE?

Topic
Solving equations

Key Question
How can determine the number of units in a case based on what you ordered and what you received?

Learning Goals
Students will:
- translate orders and shipments into cup and spacer models and algebraic equations,
- manipulate models to solve equations, and
- learn methods of solving equations by translating manipulated solutions into algebraic solutions.

Guiding Documents
Project 2061 Benchmark
- *An equation containing a variable may be true for just one value of the variable.*

NCTM Standards 2000*
- *Develop an initial conceptual understanding of different uses of variables*
- *Use symbolic algebra to represent situations and to solve problems, especially those that involve linear relationships*
- *Recognize and generate equivalent forms for simple algebraic expressions and solve linear equations*

Math
Algebra
    variables
    solving equations
        one-step equations
        multi-step equations

Integrated Processes
Observing
Comparing and contrasting
Generalizing

Materials
Case Intro animation (see *Management 2*)
Small cups (portion cups)
Tile spacers
Plastic bags
Student pages

Background Information
Traditionally, students are taught a set of procedures for solving equations. Students have difficulty because there is no apparent reason for following the steps of the procedures. The steps are meaningless to them and as a result are quickly forgotten or misapplied. To complicate matters, there are multiple ways to get to the correct solution, and the procedures they are taught stress a one-way solution. Learning the abstract procedure apart from meaning makes it difficult for students to transfer their knowledge to typical applications.

Providing the context of the equality of what is ordered and the contents of the shipment received allows students to think through the process of determining an unknown value. Using the manipulatives of a cup for the unknown quantity of a case and tile spacers for units, students can act out their thinking to probe or confirm ideas.

Consider the simplest situation. A case and three separate units are received for an order of 11 units. The shipment can be shown with a cup and three tile spacers on one side of the equal sign representing the shipment. Equal to the shipment is the 11 units ordered that are represented by 11 positive tile spacers on the other side of the equal sign. Students, encouraged to move to abstract solutions, write a symbolic representation of the model, $c + 3 = 11$. The number of units in a case is what is being determined. If the three separate units on the shipment side are ignored, a case alone remains. To ignore them, they are taken away. If three fewer units were shipped, three fewer units would have been ordered. To act out this thinking, take the three separate units from the shipment side and an equal amount from the ordered side. Symbolically, this would be shown the following way:

$$c + 3 = 11$$
$$\underline{-3} \quad \underline{-3}$$
$$c \quad = \quad 8$$

After removing the three spacers from both sides, it is evident that a case is the same as eight units.

This manipulative set works exceptionally well when dealing with negative situations. Consider a situation in which 11 units are ordered and the case received is missing three units. The manipulative set-up would have a cup containing three negative tile spacers with 11 units on the other side. (Students prefer to put the negative units in the cup to show the units are missing from the case.) Students must understand that a positive unit combined with a negative unit results in a value of zero units. In this situation, students discuss throwing in or adding three positive units to the cup to fill up the case. A full case would have required an order for three more units, meaning that a full case contains 14 units. Students would write out what they modeled with the following symbols:

$$\begin{array}{r} c - 3 = 11 \\ \underline{+3 \quad +3} \\ c \quad = 14 \end{array}$$

Another situation arises when multiple cases come in a shipment. Consider the situation when two cases are delivered when 10 units were ordered. At the manipulative level, two cups are set opposite 10 units. To determine what is in a case, split the units into two even piles. Symbolically, the students need to show that both sides were split in two to show that one case has five units.

$$\frac{2c}{2} = \frac{10}{2}$$
$$c = 5$$

The previous situations (found in sections one and two of the student pages) have all used inverse operations to get a single case alone. This is the process used for all solutions, though multiple inverse operations will be used for more complex multi-step problems.

Section three looks at two-step solutions. Two examples are discussed. *You get two cases missing a total of five units when you order nine units.* Two cups with five negative tile spacers are opposite nine positive tile spacers. Five positive tile spacers are added to both sides to fill up the cases. Next, the sides are split into two equal groups to find the amount in one case. Symbolically, this is shown:

$$\begin{array}{r} 2c - 5 = 9 \\ \underline{+5 \quad +5} \\ \frac{2c}{2} = \frac{14}{2} \\ c \quad = 7 \end{array}$$

You get four cases and six units when you order six cases. Four cups with six positive tile spacers are opposite six cups. Ignoring or removing the four shipped cases and then splitting both sides in two gives three units per case. Symbolically, this is shown:

$$\begin{array}{r} 4c + 6 = 6c \\ \underline{-4c \qquad -4c} \\ \frac{6}{2} = \frac{2c}{2} \\ 3 = c \end{array}$$

Section four looks at multi-step solutions with the variable on both sides. *You order three cases and seven units but get the same amount in five cases missing a total of three units.* Three cups with seven positive tile spacers are opposite five cups and three positive tile spacers. Most students get rid of three cups from both sides so there are two cups on only

one side. Then they fill in the cases by adding three positive tile spacers to both sides. Finally, they split both sides into two even groups to find out what is in a case. Symbolically, this is shown:

$$\begin{array}{r} 3c + 7 = 5c - 3 \\ \underline{-3c \qquad -3c} \\ 7 = 2c - 3 \\ \underline{+3 \qquad +3} \\ \frac{10}{2} = \frac{2c}{2} \\ 5 = c \end{array}$$

Section five looks at multi-step solutions that require distribution. The first example is: *You get two shipments with three cases and an extra unit in each shipment when you ordered 20 units. What's in a case?* The manipulative representation has two groups of three cups and a tile spacer across from 20 tile spacers. Many students, when looking at the manipulative, see that they can split the two sides into two even groups and they skip the distribution altogether. Symbolically, this is shown:

$$\begin{array}{r} \frac{2(3c - 1)}{2} = \frac{20}{2} \\ 3c + 1 = 10 \\ \underline{-1 \quad -1} \\ \frac{3c}{3} = \frac{9}{3} \\ c = 3 \end{array}$$

The second example requires the use of the distributive property. *Three shipments with a case and three extra units in each shipment have the same amount as two shipments two cases plus two units. What's in a case?* Now there are groups on both sides of the manipulative. Students see the distribution as just combining the contents of the groups. Three groups of a cup and three spacers are seen as three cups and nine spacers. The opposite side with two groups of two cups and two spacers is likewise seen as four cups and four spacers. To make sure the transfer of the meaning of the distributive property is made to the abstract, emphasize that students write down two equations—the description with the groups and the groups combined like the following:

$$3(c + 3) = 2(2c + 2)$$
$$3c + 9 = 4c + 4$$

Management
1. The teacher instruction video *Part Three: Equalities* is on the accompanying DVD. It is also available at the following URL: www.aimsedu.org/media/books/. It provides the rationale and suggestions for using this activity successfully in your classroom.
2. The animation *Case Intro* is on the accompanying DVD and at the URL listed above. Make preparations in your classroom so students can view the animation. If viewing through a computer, a projector enhances the experience.

3. This investigation works best with small groups of two to four students sharing material. The collaboration generates more ideas and development of understanding.

4. Each group will need a set of manipulative materials. Prepare these beforehand and place them in small plastic bags. Each set needs 10 small portion cups to represent cases (*c*). Each set needs 25 positive units and 25 negative units. Tile spacers are used for units. Negative units are made by cutting off two sides of the cross to turn a plus into a negative symbol. Tile spacers are found at any home improvement store.

5. This investigation has multiple parts that should be spread over an extended period of time. Sections one and two deal with one-step solutions. Section three deals with two-step solutions and section four deals with multi-step solutions. Section five introduces solutions with distribution. Each section has student pages that use the manipulative materials to develop conceptual understanding— 1a, 1c, 2a, 3a, 3b, 4a, 5a—and student pages to practice and reinforce student understanding—1b, 1d, 2b, 3c, 4b, 5b.

Procedure
The procedure is the same for each section of conceptual development.

1. If available, show the students the *Case Intro* animation.

2. Make sure the students are familiar with the context and the manipulative connection. They must understand that the number of units ordered is equal to the number of units delivered and that for shipment, units are placed in boxes or cases that have equal numbers of units. The object is to determine how many units are in each case without getting to look in a case. Tell students that a cup represents a case and positive tile spacers represent units while negative tile spacers represent units missing.

3. Have students read each situation on the conceptual development page and place the manipulatives on the sorting page to represent the situation.

4. Referring to the manipulative page, have students write an algebraic equation that describes the situation and manipulative representation.

5. Have the students consider how they would get a single cup (case) by itself and have them act on the manipulative one step at a time.

6. For each step done to the manipulatives, instruct the students to record symbolically what they did.

7. When students have completed the page, have them generalize what they did at the stage to get the solution.

8. Have students complete the reinforcement page referring to the context or manipulatives when having difficulty.

9. Refer students to similar problems in their textbooks and have them translate the problems into this context before using their generalizations to solve the problems. In this way they will have a context and manipulatives to refer to if they have difficulty.

Connecting Learning
1. How do you get rid of extra units? [take them away, subtract them]
2. How do you get do get rid of missing units? [add positive units to fill the cases]
3. What do you do to determine what's in a case when you have several cases? [divide things up into equal groups]
4. When you look at the equations, how do you get rid of something that was added? ...subtracted? ...multiplied? [subtract an equal amount, add and equal amount, divide into equal size groups, use the inverse operation]

Extension
Have students develop their own *What's in a Case?* problems using the manipulative to develop a key. Then have them exchange and solve each other's problems.

Solutions

What's in a Case? (1a)
1. $c = 2$	2. $c = 5$
3. $c = 5$	4. $c = 6$
5. $c = 8$	6. $c = 9$
7. $c = 5$	8. $c = 6$

What's in a Case? (1b)
1. $c = 5$	2. $c = 7$
3. $c = 5$	4. $c = 6$
5. $c = 4$	6. $c = 6$
7. $c = 12$	8. $c = 9$
9. $c = 9$	10. $c = 19$
11. $c = 6$	12. $c = 13$
13. $c = 6$	14. $c = 12$
15. $c = 9$	16. $c = 6$

What's in a Case? (1c)
1. $c = 10$	2. $c = 12$
3. $c = 10$	4. $c = 12$
5. $c = 12$	6. $c = 12$
7. $c = 8$	8. $c = 10$

What's in a Case? (1d)
1. $c = 10$	2. $c = 12$
3. $c = 8$	4. $c = 12$
5. $c = 9$	6. $c = 10$
7. $c = 5$	8. $c = 16$
9. $c = 24$	10. $c = 4$
11. $c = 20$	12. $c = 8$
13. $c = 20$	14. $c = 22$
15. $c = 25$	16. $c = 12$

What's in a Case? (2a)
1. $c = 2$	2. $c = 5$
3. $c = 3$	4. $c = 5$
5. $c = 3$	6. $c = 2$
7. $c = 6$	8. $c = 3$

What's in a Case? (2b)
1. $c = 13$	2. $c = 7$
3. $c = 15$	4. $c = 9$
5. $c = 7$	6. $c = 28$
7. $c = 6$	8. $c = 25$
9. $c = 3.5$	10. $c = 24$
11. $c = 42$	12. $c = 6$
13. $c = 4$	14. $c = 3.5$
15. $c = 10$	16. $c = 12$

What's in a Case? (3a)
1. $c = 2$	2. $c = 3$
3. $c = 7$	4. $c = 5$
5. $c = 3$	6. $c = 3$
7. $c = 4$	8. $c = 5$

What's in a Case? (3b)
1. $c = 5$	2. $c = 3$
3. $c = 3$	4. $c = 5$
5. $c = 3$	6. $c = 4$
7. $c = 3$	8. $c = 10$

What's in a Case? (3c)
1. $c = 3$ 2. $c = 6$
3. $c = 5$ 4. $c = 9$
5. $c = 15$ 6. $c = 7$
7. $c = 11$ 8. $c = 5$
9. $c = 3$ 10. $c = 5$
11. $c = 4$ 12. $c = 5$
13. $c = 8$ 14. $c = 7$
15. $c = 4$ 16. $c = 9$

What's in a Case? (4a)
1. $c = 5$ 2. $c = 3$
3. $c = 4$ 4. $c = 6$
5. $c = 7$ 6. $c = 4$
7. $c = 2$ 8. $c = 3$

What's in a Case? (4b)
1. $c = 6$ 2. $c = 7$
3. $c = 8$ 4. $c = 9$
5. $c = 8$ 6. $c = 3$
7. $c = 2$ 8. $c = 5$
9. $c = 10$ 10. $c = 7$
11. $c = 2$ 12. $c = 5$
13. $c = 3$ 14. $c = 3.5$
15. $c = 9.5$ 16. $c = 7.5$

What's in a Case? (5a)
1. $c = 3$ 2. $c = 4$
3. $c = 5$ 4. $c = 6$
5. $c = 4$ 6. $c = 2$
7. $c = 8$ 8. $c = 4$

What's in a Case? (5b)
1. $c = 5$ 2. $c = 3$
3. $c = 6$ 4. $c = 6$
5. $c = 12$ 6. $c = 6$
7. $c = 5$ 8. $c = 8$
9. $c = 7$ 10. $c = 6$
11. $c = 5$ 12. $c = 5$
13. $c = 3$ 14. $c = 3$
15. $c = 10$ 16. $c = 12$

*   Reprinted with permission from *Principles and Standards for School Mathematics*, 2000 by the National Council of Teachers of Mathematics. All rights reserved.

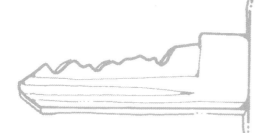

Key Question

How can determine the number of units in a case based on what you ordered and what you received?

Learning Goals

Students will:

- translate orders and shipments into cup and spacer models and algebraic equations,

- manipulate models to solve equations, and

- learn methods of solving equations by translating manipulated solutions into algebraic solutions.

SOLVING EQUATIONS: A CONCEPTUAL APPROACH

WHAT'S IN A CASE?

=

WHAT YOU ORDERED

WHAT YOU GET

WHAT'S IN A CASE?

Use your cups and spacers to build a model of each problem. Use your materials to solve the problem and record each step with algebraic symbols.

1. You order five units. You get a case and three units. What's in a case?

2. You order nine units. You get four units and a case. What's in a case?

3. You order seven units. You get a case and two units. What's in a case?

4. You order 11 units. You get five units and a case. What's in a case?

Each situation is written in algebraic symbols. Make a model with your cups and spacers and solve the problem, recording each step with algebraic symbols.

5. $c + 3 = 11$

6. $6 + c = 15$

7. $c + 1 = 6$

8. $2 + c = 8$

THE CASE

WHAT'S IN A CASE?

For each problem, apply what you have learned with your cups and spacers and show what you would do to solve what is in a case. You may use your cups and spacers to confirm your solutions.

1. $12 + c = 17$

2. $c + 8 = 15$

3. $c + 4 = 9$

4. $8 + c = 14$

5. $c + 6 = 10$

6. $c + 7 = 13$

7. $3 + c = 15$

8. $8 + c = 17$

9. $5 + c = 14$

10. $c + 4 = 23$

11. $c + 3 = 9$

12. $9 + c = 22$

13. $9 + c = 15$

14. $7 + c = 19$

15. $c + 3 = 12$

16. $11 + c = 17$

THE CASE

105

WHAT'S IN A CASE?

Use your cups and spacers to build a model of each problem. Use your materials to solve the problem and record each step with algebraic symbols.

1. You order eight units. You get a case missing two units. What's in a case?

2. You order eight units. You get a case missing four units. What's in a case?

3. You order seven units. You get a case missing three units. What's in a case?

4. You order seven units. You get a case missing five units. What's in a case?

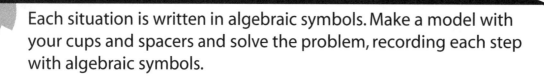

Each situation is written in algebraic symbols. Make a model with your cups and spacers and solve the problem, recording each step with algebraic symbols.

5. $c - 3 = 9$

6. $c - 2 = 10$

7. $c - 5 = 3$

8. $c - 4 = 6$

WHAT'S IN A CASE?

For each problem, apply what you have learned with your cups and spacers and show what you would do to solve what is in a case. You may use your cups and spacers to confirm your solutions.

1. $c - 2 = 8$

2. $c - 3 = 9$

3. $c - 3 = 5$

4. $c - 2 = 10$

5. $c - 4 = 5$

6. $c - 2 = 8$

7. $c - 2 = 3$

8. $c - 7 = 9$

9. $c - 10 = 14$

10. $c + 7 = 11$

11. $c - 9 = 11$

12. $c + 7 = 15$

13. $c + 6 = 26$

14. $c - 5 = 17$

15. $c + 17 = 42$

16. $c - 2.25 = 9.75$

107

WHAT'S IN A CASE?

Use your cups and spacers to build a model of each problem. Use your materials to solve the problem and record each step with algebraic symbols.

1. You order six units. You get three cases. What's in a case?

2. You order 10 units. You get two cases. What's in a case?

3. You order 12 units. You get four cases. What's in a case?

4. You order 15 units. You get three cases. What's in a case?

Each situation is written in algebraic symbols. Make a model with your cups and spacers and solve the problem, recording each step with algebraic symbols.

5. $3c = 9$

6. $4c = 8$

7. $2c = 12$

8. $5c = 15$

WHAT'S IN A CASE?

For each problem, apply what you have learned with your cups and spacers and show what you would do to solve what is in a case. You may use your cups and spacers to confirm your solutions.

1. $3c = 39$

2. $5c = 35$

3. $c + 8 = 23$

4. $2c = 18$

5. $8c = 56$

6. $c + 14 = 42$

7. $9c = 54$

8. $c - 13 = 12$

9. $2c = 7$

10. $c + 5 = 29$

11. $c + 13 = 55$

12. $1.5c = 9$

13. $2.5c = 10$

14. $4c = 14$

15. $(½)c = 5$

16. $(¾)c = 9$

109

WHAT'S IN A CASE?

Use your cups and spacers to build a model of each problem. Use your materials to solve the problem and record each step with algebraic symbols.

1. You order 11 units. You get three cases and five units. What's in a case?

2. You order nine units. You get two cases and three units. What's in a case?

3. You order nine units. You get two cases missing a total of five units. What's in a case?

4. You order eight units. You get three cases missing a total of seven units. What's in a case?

Each situation is written in algebraic symbols. Make a model with your cups and spacers and solve the problem, recording each step with algebraic symbols.

5. $4c + 3 = 15$

6. $5c + 3 = 18$

7. $4c - 3 = 13$

8. $5c - 7 = 18$

THE CASE

WHAT'S IN A CASE?

Use your cups and spacers to build a model of each problem. Use your materials to solve the problem and record each step with algebraic symbols.

1. You order three cases. You get two cases and five units. What's in a case?

2. You order six cases. You get four cases and six units. What's in a case?

3. You order two cases. You get four cases missing a total of six units. What's in a case?

4. You order four cases. You get five cases minus a total of five units. What's in a case?

Each situation is written in algebraic symbols. Make a model with your cups and spacers and solve the problem, recording each step with algebraic symbols.

5. $3c + 15 = 8c$

6. $c + 12 = 4c$

7. $9c - 15 = 4c$

8. $4c - 10 = 3c$

WHAT'S IN A CASE?

For each problem, apply what you have learned with your cups and spacers and show what you would do to solve what is in a case. You may use your cups and spacers to confirm your solutions.

1. $5c + 2 = 17$

2. $4c + 7 = 31$

3. $3c - 5 = 2c$

4. $7c - 13 = 50$

5. $2c - 7 = 23$

6. $8c - 14 = 6c$

7. $3c + 2 = 35$

8. $12c - 25 = 7c$

9. $3c + 9 = 6c$

10. $2c + 10 = 4c$

11. $15c + 7 = 67$

12. $5c + 20 = 9c$

13. $4c - 6 = 26$

14. $6c - 7 = 35$

15. $4c + 12 = 7c$

16. $26c - 27 = 23c$

WHAT'S IN A CASE?

Use your cups and spacers to build a model of each problem. Use your materials to solve the problem and record each step with algebraic symbols.

1. You order three cases and seven units. You get five cases missing a total of three units. What's in a case?

2. You order five cases and nine units. You get seven cases and three units. What's in a case?

3. You order three cases and nine units. You get six cases missing a total of three units. What's in a case?

4. You order four cases and ten units. You get five cases and four units. What's in a case?

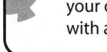

Each situation is written in algebraic symbols. Make a model with your cups and spacers and solve the problem, recording each step with algebraic symbols.

5. $2c + 5 = 3c - 2$

6. $4c - 3 = 2c + 5$

7. $3c + 5 = 5c + 1$

8. $5c - 4 = 3c + 2$

113

WHAT'S IN A CASE?

For each problem, apply what you have learned with your cups and spacers and show what you would do to solve what is in a case. You may use your cups and spacers to confirm your solutions.

1. $15c - 12 = 8c + 30$

2. $11c + 3 = 8c + 24$

3. $7 + 4c = 9c - 33$

4. $7c + 15 = 9c - 3$

5. $15 + 7c = 5c + 31$

6. $27c + 4 = 15c + 40$

7. $15c - 3 = 6c + 15$

8. $12c - 8 = 5c + 27$

9. $7c + 63 = 15c - 17$

10. $32c + 13 = 27c + 48$

11. $23c + 7 = 14c + 25$

12. $12c - 15 = 5c + 20$

13. $7c + 4 = 34 - 3c$

14. $3c - 5 = c + 2$

15. $13c + 33 = 17c - 5$

16. $13c + 23 = 17c - 7$

WHAT'S IN A CASE?

Use your cups and spacers to build a model of each problem. Use your materials to solve the problem and record each step with algebraic symbols.

1. You order 20 units. You get two shipments with three cases and an extra unit in each shipment. What's in a case?

2. You order 14 units. You get two shipments of one unit short of two cases. What's in a case?

3. Three shipments with a case and three extra units in each shipment are equal to two shipments of two cases plus two units. What's in a case?

4. Two shipments of two units short of three cases are equal to four shipments of a case plus two units. What's in a case?

Each situation is written in algebraic symbols. Make a model with your cups and spacers and solve the problem, recording each step with algebraic symbols.

5. $3(2c - 3) = 15$

6. $3(3c + 1) = 21$

7. $4(c + 1) = 3(2c - 4)$

8. $3(2c - 4) = 2(2c - 2)$

THE CASE

WHAT'S IN A CASE?

For each problem, apply what you have learned with your cups and spacers and show what you would do to solve what is in a case. You may use your cups and spacers to confirm your solutions.

1. $5(3c - 6) = 45$

2. $2(6c - 5) = 26$

3. $3(4c - 4) = 60$

4. $2(4c - 6) = 36$

5. $5(c + 2) = 2(2c + 11)$

6. $6(2c + 2) = 4(2c + 9)$

7. $2(5c + 2) = 3(4c - 2)$

8. $6(2c - 1) = 5(2c + 2)$

9. $5(2c - 6) = 40$

10. $3(3c - 2) = 4(3c - 6)$

11. $4(3c - 6) = 36$

12. $2(4c - 1) = 38$

13. $2(7c + 3) = 3(6c - 2)$

14. $3(3c + 2) = 33$

15. $5(3c + 2) = 4(5c - 10)$

16. $7(2c + 3) = 3(5c + 3)$

WHAT'S IN A CASE?

Connecting Learning

1. How do you get rid of extra units?

2. How do you get do get rid of missing units

3. What do you do to determine what's in a case when you have several cases?

4. When you look at the equations, how do you get rid of something that was added? ...subtracted? ...multiplied?

117

TRACKING TREASURE TWO

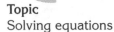

Topic
Solving equations

Key Question
How do you use a clue with multiple steps to determine under which palm to dig for the buried treasure?

Learning Goals
Students will:
* recognize that working backwards through an instruction leads to the original condition, and
* become skilled at working backwards numerically though a multiple step procedure of basic operations using inverse operations.

Guiding Documents
Project 2061 Benchmarks
* *Mathematics is the study of many kinds of patterns, including numbers and shapes and operations on them. Sometimes patterns are studied because they help to explain how the world works or how to solve practical problems, sometimes because they are interesting in themselves.*
* *In using mathematics, choices have to be made about what operations will give the best results. Results should always be judged by whether they make sense and are useful.*
* *Add, subtract, multiply, and divide whole numbers mentally, on paper, and with a calculator.*
* *State the purpose of each step in a calculation.*

NCTM Standards 2000*
* *Identify and use relationships between operations, such as division as the inverse of multiplication, to solve problems*
* *Describe, extend, and make generalizations about geometric and numeric patterns*
* *Represent the idea of a variable as an unknown quantity using a letter or a symbol*
* *Express mathematical relationships using equations*

Math
Number
    inverse operations
Algebra
    solving equations
        multi-step equations

Integrated Processes
Observing
Comparing and contrasting
Generalizing
Applying

Materials
Tracks2 Intro animation (see *Management 1*)
Student pages
Game pieces (cubes, pennies, bingo markers)
Scissors
Tape or glue

Background Information
To solve equations, students need to understand that to undo an operation, its inverse operation is used. To undo the operation of making two steps forward from a position $(x + 2)$, you just take two steps backward $(x + 2 - 2 = x)$.

Equality is the second idea required to solve equations. If two steps forward gets you to the seventh position $(x + 2 = 7)$, then taking away two steps will get you back to the original position $(x + 2 - 2 = 7 - 2)$. Since the instruction and the outcome are equal, when you take something from the instruction, you must do the same to the outcome to keep the equality. In our example, the original position was five $(x = 5)$. This investigation provides a context in which students can act out the situation. As students act out the problems, they develop an understanding of the meaning of the abstract record.

This investigation is based on the following scenario:
> *A pirate has buried a treasure on an island with 51 palm trees planted in a row. He has left you only one clue that has a sequence of instructions. Be the first to determine under which tree he has buried the treasure to win the prize.*

Management
1. The animation *Tracks2 Intro* is on the accompanying DVD. It is also available at the following URL: www.aimsedu.org/media/books/. Make preparations in your classroom so students can view the animation. If viewing through a computer, a projector enhances the experience.
2. This investigation deals with multi-step solutions to equations. If students are not familiar with one-step solutions, they should do *Tracking Treasure One* prior to doing this activity. If students have not done *Part One* but are familiar with one-step solutions, an abbreviated experience of *Part One* is appropriate before they do *Part Two*.
3. Make a copy of the island number line for each student. The students will cut the page into three strips and glue or tape the strips together to form a number line. Each student can act out the reverse sequence on his or her number line with a game piece.

4. Pairs of students work best for this investigation, although groups of four are manageable. In a group of four, students can form teams of two. Some teachers find that pairing a stronger student with a weaker one helps.
5. Prepare a set of cards for each group. There are two sets. The first is a sequence of operations. These should be used with students to develop the idea of multiple steps. The second set is instructions that are formatted into typical algebraic form and will help students prepare for more abstract equations. For both sets, cut the cards apart on the bold lines and fold on the dotted lines.

Procedure

1. If available, show the students the *Tracks2 Intro* animation.
2. Distribute the island number line page, scissors, and tape or glue. Have the students assemble the number line by cutting the page into three strips of trees and numbers. Instruct them to glue the number line in order to form a long strip.
3. Explain to the class the scenario and have them use game pieces and their number lines to work backward through the following sequence to find under which tree the treasure is buried: $((x + 8) \cdot 3) - 30 = -12$ $x = -2$
4. Practice several times until students are successful. Several sequences follow:
$((x \div 3) - 3) \cdot 6 = 24$ $x = 21$
$((x \cdot 2) - 22) \div 3 = -2$ $x = 8$
$((x + 6) \div 3) + 13 = 10$ $x = -15$
5. Have the student break into groups to play the game. The cards are placed in a stack like tents with the equation on the top card facing the students. The

$(x \cdot 2) + 7 = 25$

students all sit with their number lines so they can see only the equation on the top card of the stack. All the students move the game pieces to determine where the treasure is buried and declare their selections. When all the students have a solution, the stack is turned around to expose the solution. The student who was first to determine the solution wins the round and keeps the card after the stack is turned so the equation faces forward. The game continues until the cards have all been won. The winner of the game is the student with the highest sum value of treasures (x). An alternate version is to have students find the sum of the absolute values of the x values.
6. Have the students discuss how the clues might be simplified. (If the class is not familiar with combining like terms, order of operations, and the distributive property, consider doing *Widgets, Inc.* before continuing.) Have the class practice on the samples.

$$((x \div 3) - 3) \cdot 6 = 6\left(\frac{x}{3} - 3\right) = 2x - 18 = 24 \quad x = 21$$

$$((x \cdot 2) - 22) \div 3 = \frac{2x - 22}{3} = -2 \qquad x = 8$$

$$((x + 6) \div 3) + 13 \quad \frac{x + 6}{3} + 13 = 10 \qquad x = -15$$

$$((x + 8) \cdot 3) - 30 = 3(x + 8) - 30 =$$
$$3x + 24 - 30 = 3x - 6 = -12 \qquad x = -2$$

7. Have the students play the game again with the simplified set of equations.
8. Provide individual practice for the students by having them complete the practice pages.

Connecting Learning

1. How do you find the value of x when you have a sequence of instructions? [Backtrack through the instructions in reverse sequence using the inverse operation.]
2. How do you find the value of x when the instructions have been simplified into algebraic form? [Backtrack through the instructions in reverse order of the order of operations using the inverse operation.]

Extension

Students may make up their own equation that needs to be solved to determine under which tree the treasure is hidden. Students can then exchange equations and determine where the other student has hidden the treasure.

Solutions
Practice One
What do you call a buccaneer who is good at geometry?
  ARGH A PI-RAT

1. A	$x = -25$	2. R	$x = 8$
3. G	$x = -13$	4. H	$x = -11$
5. A	$x = -25$	6. P	$x = 4$
7. I	$x = -9$	8. R	$x = 8$
9. A	$x = -25$	10. T	$x = 12$

Practice Two
Why do geometrical buccaneers collect gold coins?
  PI-RATS LOVE CIRCLES

1. P	$x = -4$	2. I	$x = 9$
3. R	$x = -8$	4. A	$x = 25$
5. T	$x = -12$	6. S	$x = -10$
7. L	$x = 3$	8. O	$x = -2$
9. V	$x = -16$	10. E	$x = 17$
11. C	$x = 21$		

* Reprinted with permission from *Principles and Standards for School Mathematics*, 2000 by the National Council of Teachers of Mathematics. All rights reserved.

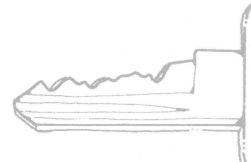

Key Question

How do you use a clue with multiple steps to determine under which palm to dig for the buried treasure?

Learning Goals

Students will:

- recognize that working backwards through an instruction leads to the original condition, and
- become skilled at working backwards numerically though a multiple step procedure of basic operations using inverse operations.

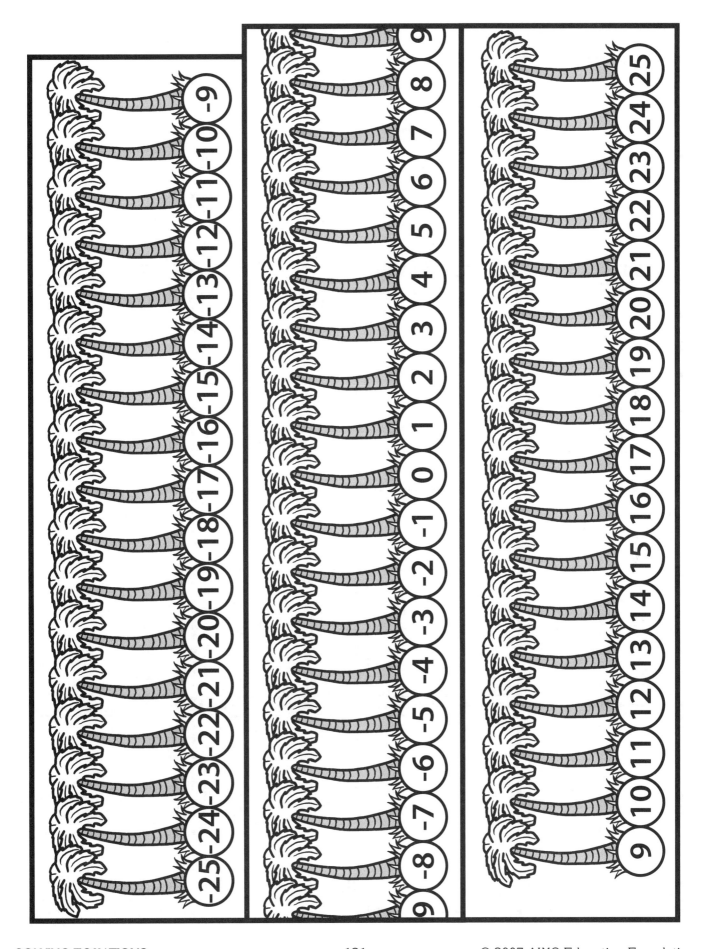

MULTI-STEP SEQUENCE CARDS

$x = 25$ $((x \div 5) + 7) \cdot 2) - 4 = 20$	$x = 10$ $(x - 5) \cdot 3) + 6 = 21$	$x = -4$ $(x \div 2) + 10 = 8$	$x = 5$ $(x + 2) \cdot 2 = 14$
$x = -20$ $((x \div 4) + 3) \cdot 8) + 3 = -13$	$x = -8$ $(x + 10) \cdot 8) - 3 = 13$	$x = 9$ $(x - 3) \cdot 5 = 15$	$x = 9$ $(x - 2) \cdot 5 = 20$
$x = 18$ $((x + 2) \div 5) - 1) \cdot 7 = 21$	$x = 14$ $(x + 6) \div 5) - 9 = -5$	$x = 11$ $(x - 5) \cdot 2 = 12$	$x = 3$ $(x \cdot 3) - 12 = -3$
$x = -22$ $((x - 3) \div 5) + 7) \cdot 6 = 12$	$x = -12$ $(x + 4) \cdot 2) - 9 = -25$	$x = 6$ $(x \cdot 2) + 7 = 25$	$x = -2$ $(x \cdot 5) + 12 = 2$

MULTI-STEP SIMPLIFIED CARDS

$\dfrac{x}{5} - 12 = -7$ ¦ $25 = x$	$\dfrac{2x-3}{3} = 3$ ¦ $6 = x$	$3(x-2) = 15$ ¦ $7 = x$	$3x + 2 = 14$ ¦ $4 = x$
$5(x-2)+4 = -21$ ¦ $-3 = x$	$\dfrac{x-2}{3} + 5 = 9$ ¦ $14 = x$	$5(x+5) = 15$ ¦ $-2 = x$	$2x - 17 = 7$ ¦ $12 = x$
$\dfrac{x+2}{3} = 6$ ¦ $16 = x$	$2\left(\dfrac{x}{3}\right) + 5 = 9$ ¦ $6 = x$	$\dfrac{x-2}{3} = 5$ ¦ $17 = x$	$4x + 15 = -9$ ¦ $-6 = x$
$\dfrac{x}{3} + 5 = 8$ ¦ $9 = x$	$5(x+7)+3 = 13$ ¦ $-5 = x$	$\dfrac{x}{3} + 7 = 2$ ¦ $-15 = x$	$2x - 7 = 13$ ¦ $10 = x$

TRACKING TREASURE TWO

PRACTICE ONE

Solve each equation. Take the solution and use the table at the bottom of the page to find its letter equivalent. Put the letter in the box for the equation number to find the answer to the question.

What do you call a buccaneer who is good at geometry?

1.	2.	3.	4.	5.	6.	7.	8.	9.	10.
						—			

1. $(x + 10) \div 3 = -5$

2. $(x \div 4) \cdot 6 = 12$

3. $(x + 1) \div (-3) = 4$

4. $(x + 2) \div 3 = -3$

5. $(x \div 5) - 3 = -8$

6. $(x \cdot 3) + 5 = 17$

7. $((x + 1) \div 4) + 7 = 5$

8. $((x - 2) \cdot 4) + 1 = 25$

9. $((x \div 5) + 12) \cdot 3 = 21$

10. $((x \div 4) - 9) \cdot 3 = -18$

-25	-23	-21	-19	-17	-15	-13	-11	-9	-7	-5	-3	-1	0	2	4	6	8	10	12	14	16	18	20	22	24
A	B	C	D	E	F	G	H	I	J	K	L	M	N	O	P	Q	R	S	T	U	V	W	X	Y	Z

TRACKING TREASURE TWO

PRACTICE TWO

Solve each equation. Take the solution and use the table at the bottom of the page to find its letter equivalent. Put the letter in the box for the equation number to find the answer to the question.

Why do geometrical buccaneers collect gold coins?

1.	2.	3.	4.	5.	6.	7.	8.	9.	10.	11.

11.	2.	3.	11.	7.	10.	6.

1. $2x + 15 = 7$

2. $2x - 13 = 5$

3. $3x + 11 = -13$

4. $\frac{x}{5} - 9 = -4$

5. $2x + 39 = 15$

6. $2x - 5 = -25$

7. $7x - 10 = 11$

8. $\frac{6x}{3} + 2 = -2$

9. $\frac{x+4}{3} + 4 = 0$

10. $\frac{x-2}{3} + 14 = 19$

11. $\frac{x-6}{3} + 2 = 7$

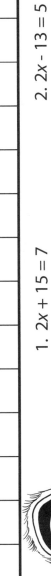

25	23	21	19	17	15	13	11	9	7	5	3	1	0	-2	-4	-6	-8	-10	-12	-14	-16	-18	-20	-22	-24
A	B	C	D	E	F	G	H	I	J	K	L	M	N	O	P	Q	R	S	T	U	V	W	X	Y	Z

TRACKING TREASURE TWO

Connecting Learning

1. How do you find the value of x when you have a sequence of instructions?

2. How do you find the value of x when the instructions have been simplified into algebraic form?

POGO STICK PATHS

Topic
Solving equations

Key Question
How can you determine the length of a pogo stick jump by knowing how many times each person jumped and how far they dragged their pogo sticks?

Learning Goals
Students will:
- translate a picture of pogo stick jumpers into an equation,
- determine the length of a jump from the context of a story, and
- generalize the steps for solving a story for use in solving equations.

Guiding Documents
Project 2061 Benchmarks
- *An equation containing a variable may be true for just one value of the variable.*
- *Mathematical statements can be used to describe how one quantity changes when another changes. Rates of change can be computed from magnitudes and vice versa.*
- *The operations + and – are inverses of each other— one undoes what the other does; likewise x and ÷.*

NCTM Standards 2000*
- *Develop an initial conceptual understanding of different uses of variables*
- *Use symbolic algebra to represent situations and to solve problems, especially those that involve linear relationships*
- *Recognize and generate equivalent forms for simple algebraic expressions and solve linear equations*

Math
Algebra
    solving equations
        systems of equations

Integrated Processes
Observing
Comparing and contrasting
Generalizing

Materials
White board
White board markers (two colors)

Student pages
Meter stick, optional
Tape, optional

Background Information
Students need concrete experiences with which to relate their thinking. Simulations of pogo stick jumps provide a context to which students can relate their thinking. The context is about two friends who jump on their pogo sticks together. Markers simulate the pogo sticks and each dot left on a white board represents the print left behind. Attaching a meter stick to the white board, the teacher can "jump" the two markers down the board, leaving two sets of prints the same distance apart on the board. If one pogo stick stops jumping earlier than the other, the two friends would get back together dragging their pogo sticks, leaving a line in the dirt or on the board. By looking at the pogo stick markings on the board, the students will solve how long a jump is and will relate that to the process of solving equations.

Consider the example of one jumper making four jumps and then draging the pogo stick nine centimeters, while the second jumper makes seven jumps and drags the pogo stick back three centimeters. What the teacher would put on the board would look like this drawing:

When asked to look at the record of the story and figure out the length of a jump, students suggest ignoring or crossing out the first jumps because they are the same. The difference in the two jumpers is the three extra jumps the second friend made. The three jumps gave 12 cm of extra distance (nine forward and three back is 12). So if three jumps make the second jumper go 12 extra centimeters, every jump had to be four centimeters. This is determined by splitting (dividing) the 12 centimeters into three even jumps.

The students' line of thinking is easily modeled with algebra. The expression for the first jumper is $4j + 9$ where j represents the length of the jump. The second jumper's expression is $7j - 3$. Since both jumpers end up at the same place, these expressions are equal. ($4j + 9 = 7j - 3$) To solve for j, the students do the same algebraic steps that they followed in their thinking. They ignore or remove the first four jumps by subtracting them from both expressions. Then they add the distances together to see how far the second jumper moved with three jumps. Finally, they divide the distance of 12 by three to determine how long one jump is.

$$
\begin{array}{r}
4j + 9 = 7j - 3 \\
-4j \quad\quad -4j \\
\hline
9 = 3j - 3 \\
+3 \quad\quad +3 \\
\hline
12 = 3j \\
\overline{3} \quad\quad \overline{3} \\
4 = j
\end{array}
$$

Initially, students may only follow the line of thinking with the visual record. The teacher may need to model their thinking with the algebraic symbols. As students mimic the teacher, they begin to recognize how each step of their thinking is symbolized. When the symbols have meaning for the students, they begin to manipulate the symbols as they do the visual representation of the context. With practice, the sequence becomes so routine that students begin to operate on the symbol ignoring the connection to the context. At this point, students can transfer the process to other contexts.

Management
1. Clear an area on the white board or chalkboard. If a more permanent record is desired, hang butcher paper or chart papers on a wall. You will need to simulate two people jumping together on pogo sticks. To simulate this, jump two markers across the board—one above the other—with a hump for each jump. All the jumps should be about the same length and each of the jumps of both trails should start and stop in the same position. You will need to make the jumps accurately while telling the story to the class. This will take some practice before class to become comfortable. You can modify the procedure by drawing each trail separately.
2. You may find it easier to keep the jumps the same lengths if they are drawn vertically. For this alternate method, hang a meter stick vertically on the board by clipping it to the map rail or taping it on the top end. With the two markers representing pogo sticks make a trail of jumps on either side of the meter stick. The meter stick will need to be moved down the board to provide a record of multiple experiences.
3. The investigation *Jumping to Solutions* should be done before this activity so the context is more familiar.

Procedure
1. Explain the scenario to the class and simulate the following story on the board. *Two friends jump down the street on their pogo sticks. Their jumps are the same length. The first one stops after four jumps, and the other makes seven jumps. To get together, the first friend drags his pogo stick nine meters farther while the second drags hers back three meters. How can you use these trails to determine how long a jump is from the information in this story?* $(4j + 9 = 7j - 3, j = 4)$
2. Have students make a sketch of the trails on the page and provide time for them to come to a solution for the problem. As students are working, move around the room to assess different approaches to the problem. As students get the solution, have them share with a partner to see if they agree on the same solution.
3. Have students share their methods of solution and reasoning. Encourage them to look for similarities and differences in approaches.
4. Model the algebraic solution for students, having them relate each algebraic step to their lines of thinking as they record the steps to the algebraic solution.
5. Continue with more simulations until the students are comfortable with the context, making a visual record, finding a solution, and translating their solution processes into algebraic form. Suggested scenarios might include: $(4j + 12 = 8j - 8, j = 5)$, $(3j + 10 = 5j - 4, j = 7)$, $(6j + 16 = 10j - 8, j = 6)$.
6. Distribute the second student page and have students translate the pictures into algebra and determine the length of the jump.
7. Distribute the third student page and have students translate the algebraic equations into a visual record and solve for the length of a jump.
8. Have students generalize the process used to solve multi-step problems with a variable on both sides of the equation.

Connecting Learning
1. How did each jumper get to the final position? [took a number of jumps and moved forward or back a distance]
2. How would you translate each of your verbal descriptions into an expression? [number of jumps · length of jump (j) +/– distance]
3. Since both jumpers ended in the same place, their movements are equal. Make an equation with the two expressions that shows their movements are equal.
4. Using your sketch, equation, or numbers, how would you determine the length of a jump?
   a. How far apart are the two friends when they stopped jumping? How did you find this distance?
   b. How many more jumps did the second jumper make than the first jumper? How did you get this number?

c. How long is each jump? How do you determine this length?
   d. How far were the two jumpers from the start when they got together?
5. What steps did you follow every time to determine the length of a jump?

Extensions

1. Have students write their own narratives about pogo stick situations and make a sketch, equation, and solution. Then have students share their narratives with each other, solve, and check.
2. Have students look at problems for solving equations in their texts that have a variable on both sides of the equation and require multiple steps. Have them discuss the similarity between the equations in the book and equations from the pogo stick situations. Have them translate the equations into jump situations and solve.

Solutions

Page One
1. $4j + 9 = 7j - 3$ $j = 4$
2. $4j + 12 = 8j - 8$ $j = 5$
3. $3j + 10 = 5j - 4$ $j = 7$
4. $6j + 16 = 10j - 8$ $j = 6$

Page Two
1. $5j + 3 = 9j - 5$ $j = 2$
2. $3j + 6 = 8j - 4$ $j = 2$
3. $10j - 4 = 4j + 14$ $j = 3$
4. $3j + 12 = 6j - 3$ $j = 5$
5. $4j + 6 = 9j - 9$ $j = 3$
6. $8j - 5 = 2j + 10$ $j = 2.5$

Page Three
1. $j = 3$
2. $j = 4$
3. $j = 6$
4. $j = 7$
5. $j = 9$
6. $j = 2$
7. $j = 4.5$
8. $j = 5.5$

*   Reprinted with permission from *Principles and Standards for School Mathematics*, 2000 by the National Council of Teachers of Mathematics. All rights reserved.

POGO STICK PATHS

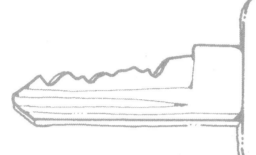

Key Question

How can you determine the length of a pogo stick jump by knowing how many times each person jumped and how far they dragged their pogo sticks?

Learning Goals

Students will:

- translate a picture of pogo stick jumpers into an equation,

- determine the length of a jump from the context of a story, and

- generalize the steps for solving a story for use in solving equations.

130

POGO STICK PATHS

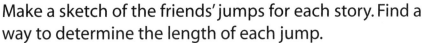
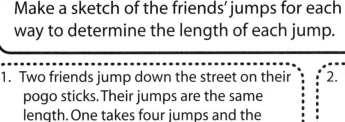

Make a sketch of the friends' jumps for each story. Find a way to determine the length of each jump.

1. Two friends jump down the street on their pogo sticks. Their jumps are the same length. One takes four jumps and the other takes seven jumps. The first jumper drags his pogo stick nine meters forward. The second jumper drags her stick back three meters to meet her friend. How far did they go in each jump?

2. Two friends jump down the street on their pogo sticks. Their jumps are the same length. One takes four jumps and the other takes eight jumps. The first jumper drags his pogo stick 12 meters forward. The second jumper drags her stick back eight meters to meet her friend. How far did they go in each jump?

3. Two friends jump down the street on their pogo sticks. Their jumps are the same length. One takes three jumps and the other takes five jumps. The first jumper drags his pogo stick 10 meters forward. The second jumper drags her stick back four meters to meet her friend. How far did they go in each jump?

4. Two friends jump down the street on their pogo sticks. Their jumps are the same length. One takes six jumps and the other takes 10 jumps. The first jumper drags his pogo stick 16 meters forward. The second jumper drags her stick back eight meters to meet her friend. How far did they go in each jump?

POGO STICK PATHS

Translate each picture about a pogo stick story into an algebra equation. Then solve the equation to determine the length of the jumps in each problem.

1
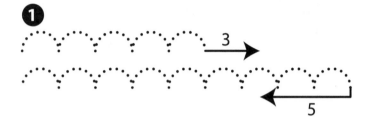

2
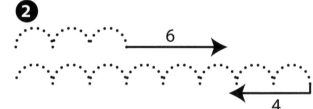

3
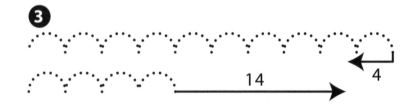

4
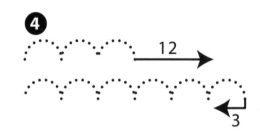

5
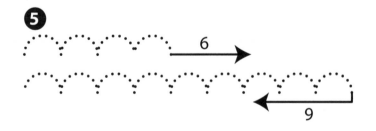

6
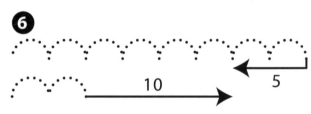

132

POGO STICK PATHS

Make a sketch of the pogo stick trails described by each equation. Then solve for the length of each jump.

1. $7j - 5 = 3j + 7$

2. $5j + 15 = 12j - 13$

3. $15j - 13 = 12j + 5$

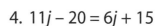

4. $11j - 20 = 6j + 15$

5. $11j + 12 = 13j - 6$

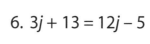

6. $3j + 13 = 12j - 5$

7. $9j - 10 = 5j + 8$

8. $8j - 10 = 5j + 6.5$

133

POGO STICK PATHS

Connecting Learning

1. How did each jumper get to the final position?

2. How would you translate each of your verbal descriptions into an expression?

3. Since both jumpers ended in the same place, their movements are equal. Make an equation with the two expressions that shows their movements are equal.

4. Using your sketch, equation, or numbers, how would you determine the length of a jump?
   a. How far apart are the two friends when they stopped jumping? How did you find this distance?
   b. How many more jumps did the second jumper make than the first jumper? How did you get this number?
   c. How long is each jump? How do you determine this length?
   d. How far were the two jumpers from the start when they got together?

5. What steps did you follow every time to determine the length of a jump?

LEVELED LOADS

Topic
Solving equations: Mixture problems

Key Question
On a balance, how can you determine what combinations of loads will balance a single load on the opposite side?

Learning Goals
Students will:
- level a balance that has multiple loads,
- recognize how a numeric equality represents a level balance,
- generalize their observations to predict and check the placement of loads on a balance, and
- apply the general equation to similar situations about mixtures.

Guiding Documents
Project 2061 Benchmarks
- *An equation containing a variable may be true for just one value of the variable.*
- *Mathematical statements can be used to describe how one quantity changes when another changes. Rates of change can be computed from magnitudes and vice versa.*
- *The operations + and – are inverses of each other—one undoes what the other does; likewise x and ÷.*

NCTM Standards 2000*
- *Develop an initial conceptual understanding of different uses of variables*
- *Use symbolic algebra to represent situations and to solve problems, especially those that involve linear relationships*
- *Recognize and generate equivalent forms for simple algebraic expressions and solve linear equations*

Math
Algebra
   solving equations
     mixtures

Integrated Processes
Observing
Comparing and contrasting
Generalizing

Materials
For the class:
   double-sided tape
   scissors

For each group:
   ruler
   1 medium binder clip
   12 small binder clips (¾" clip size)
   modeling clay (a small piece)

Background Information
If the torque on each side of a balance is equal, the balance will be level. Torque is the product of the mass of the load and the distance the load is from the point of rotation—the fulcrum.

In this investigation, the balance is made from a ruler, which allows for the measurement of distance from the fulcrum. Binder clips are used for the load, so the quantity is the measure of mass. The load can be placed at multiple positions on one side of the balance. If, on one side, two clips are placed four units from the fulcrum along with two clips placed six units from the fulcrum, 20 units of torque are generated $(2(4) + 2(6) = 20)$. One way to maintain a level balance is to put four clips five units on the other side of the fulcrum $(2(4) + 2(6) = 4(5))$.

With experience, students can come to generalize this pattern with an equation such as $Q_1(V_1) + Q_2(V_2) = Q_T(V_T)$ (where Q represents the quantity of clips and V represents the value of units from the fulcrum). An understanding of this generalized equation allows students to apply this model to any mixture problem that is based on quantity and value. The quantity is often expressed in mass or volume, while the value often involves money.

Management
1. Prepare the balances ahead of time by following the instructions on the *Balance Construction* page.
2. This investigation works well in groups of four students. One student can hold the balance while two others move the clips on each side of the balance and the fourth student records the outcomes.
3. This activity is split into three parts that can be done over consecutive days. The first part is exploratory— the students are told given quantities and locations for clips on the left side of the balance. Then they experiment with the right side to see where to put an assigned quantity of clips or how many clips

to put at an assigned position. From the exploration, students develop a generalization and use it to predict the missing quantity of clips or position of the clips. Finally, when they have confirmed their generalization, they practice its application and transfer to similar settings.

Procedure

Exploration

1. Demonstrate how the balance works. Put two clips four units from the fulcrum and two clips six units from the fulcrum on the left side of the balance.
2. Have students predict where to put four clips on the right side to make the balance level. Try their suggestions until the correct position is found (five units from the fulcrum).

3. Distribute the balances and clips and have students work through the 10 combinations listed on the chart. Multiple clips are connected in one string by attaching clips to silver wire handles. Emphasize that clips must be attached in the center of a number so that either edge of the clip just touches the opposite edges of the region.
4. When the balance is level, have the students record the quantity or position of the clips on the right side. Due to precision of clip placement, the balance may not level exactly. Have students choose the whole position or quantity of clips that brings the balance closest to level.
5. Have students discuss generalizations they can make from the investigation.

Generalization

1. Distribute the second student page.
2. Have students review what generalizations they made in the exploration part of the activity. Then ask them to predict where to place four clips on the right side of a balance in the first example, explaining their reasoning from the generalizations.
3. Distribute the balances and have students use them to confirm or disprove their predictions. If necessary, have students adjust the position to get the balance level. Tell them to record the correct position.
4. Instruct the students to work through the 10 combinations, first predicting and then confirming their predictions with the balance and recording the correct solution.

5. Have students summarize their generalizations and then record the procedure in an equation.

Application

1. Distribute the third and fourth student pages.
2. Have students review their equations and explain how to use them to solve problem number one. Have them solve the first four problems.
3. Discuss how problem five is similar to and different from problem one with the students.
4. Using the numbers in problem five in their generalized equation, have students solve the problem.
5. Have students compare the equations for problems one and six to note the two mixture problems can be solved in a similar way.
6. Instruct students to complete the remaining problems using the generalized equation.

Connecting Learning

1. What patterns do you notice in the amount or placement of clips on a level balance? [The sum of the products of the two quantities and values equals the product of the one quantity and value.]
2. How can you write your pattern as an equation? $[Q_1(V_1) + Q_2(V_2) = Q_T(V_T)]$
3. How are the balance combination problems similar to other combination problems on the application page? [Values change from position to dollars, and quantity changes from clips to pounds or gallons. The mixture of two types of quantities and values combines to make a single quantity and value.]
4. How can you use your generalized equation to solve similar problems about combinations? [Substitute the corresponding numbers for quantity and value and solve for the remaining unknown.]

Solutions

Exploration

Quantity	Value	+	Quantity	Value	=	Quantity	Value
2	4	+	2	6	=	4	**5**
2	4	+	2	5	=	3	**6**
1	8	+	3	4	=	5	**4**
1	6	+	3	8	=	**6**	5
3	7	+	3	5	=	**6**	6
2	8	+	2	6	=	4	7
2	5	+	2	7	=	6	**4**
3	6	+	2	7	=	4	8
2	4	+	1	7	=	3	**5**
2	6	+	1	4	=	**2**	8

Generalization

Quantity	Value	+	Quantity	Value	=	Quantity	Value
2	6	+	2	8	=	4	**7**
6	3	+	2	5	=	**4**	7
5	4	+	2	**6**	=	4	8
3	6	+	**3**	4	=	5	6
2	**8**	+	3	4	=	7	4
2	6	+	3	4	=	3	8
2	7	+	2	5	=	**3**	8
3	8	+	**2**	4	=	4	8
3	**7**	+	1	3	=	3	8
3	7	+	3	**5**	=	6	6

Application

1. $8(3) + 2(8) = 4(x)$
   $24 + 16 = 4x$
   $40 = 4x$
   $x = 10$

2. $5(8) = 3(4) + 7(x)$
   $40 = 12 + 7x$
   $28 = 7x$
   $x = 4$

3. $6(9) + 6(3) = 8(x)$
   $54 + 18 = 8x$
   $72 = 8x$
   $x = 9$

4. $7(x) + 7(3) = 5(7)$
   $7x + 21 = 35$
   $7x = 14$
   $x = 2$

5. $8(3) + 2(8) = 10(x)$
   $24 + 16 = 10x$
   $40 = 10x$
   $x = 4$

6. $8(4) = 6(3) + 2(x)$
   $32 = 18 + 2x$
   $14 = 2x$
   $x = 7$

7. $2(3) + 4(x) = 6(2)$
   $6 + 4x = 12$
   $4x = 6$
   $x = 1.5$

8. $3(x) + 1(8) = 4(11)$
   $3x + 8 = 44$
   $3x = 36$
   $x = 12$

9. $4(6) + 2(6) = 6(x)$
   $24 + 12 = 6x$
   $36 = 6x$
   $x = 6$

10. $2(8) + 3(10) = 5(x)$
    $16 + 30 = 5x$
    $46 = 5x$
    $x = 9.2$

LEVELED LOADS

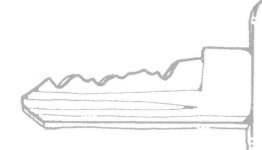

Key Question

On a balance, how can you determine what combinations of loads will balance a single load on the opposite side?

Learning Goals

Students will:

- level a balance that has multiple loads,

- recognize how a numeric equality represents a level balance,

- generalize their observations to predict and check the placement of loads on a balance, and

- apply the general equation to similar situations about mixtures.

LEVELED LOADS

1. Copy the pages of number strips onto paper or card stock.
2. Cut out the required number of strips of both types—one strip of each type per balance.
3. Attach a strip of black numbers along the left half of the smooth side of a ruler using double-sided tape or glue. The right edge of the "one" region should be at the center of the ruler and the left side of the "eight" region will extend beyond the end of the ruler.

4. Attach a strip of white numbers to the right half of the ruler in a similar manner.

5. Clip a medium binder clip to the top of the ruler so that it is centered between the black and white numbered regions. Fold back the handles of the binder clip.

6. Hang the balance on a pencil that is extended through the handles.

7. If the balance does not hang level, put a small ball of clay on the higher side of the balance so that the balance is made to hang level.

LEVELED LOADS

1	2	3	4	5	6	7	8
1	2	3	4	5	6	7	8
1	2	3	4	5	6	7	8
1	2	3	4	5	6	7	8
1	2	3	4	5	6	7	8
1	2	3	4	5	6	7	8
1	2	3	4	5	6	7	8
1	2	3	4	5	6	7	8
1	2	3	4	5	6	7	8

LEVELED LOADS

8	7	6	5	4	3	2	1
8	7	6	5	4	3	2	1
8	7	6	5	4	3	2	1
8	7	6	5	4	3	2	1
8	7	6	5	4	3	2	1
8	7	6	5	4	3	2	1
8	7	6	5	4	3	2	1
8	7	6	5	4	3	2	1
8	7	6	5	4	3	2	1

LEVELED LOADS

Put the combinations of clips and positions from the left side of the chart on the left half of your balance.

Find the number of clips or the position of clips needed on the right half to balance the ruler. Record your results on the chart.

QUANTITY OF CLIPS	VALUE OF POSITION	AND	QUANTITY OF CLIPS	VALUE OF POSITION	BALANCES	QUANTITY OF CLIPS	VALUE OF POSITION
2	4	+	2	6	=	4	
2	4	+	2	5	=	3	
1	8	+	3	4	=	5	
1	6	+	3	8	=		5
3	7	+	3	5	=		6
2	8	+	2	6	=		7
2	5	+	2	7	=	6	
3	6	+	2	7	=		8
2	4	+	1	7	=	3	
2	6	+	1	4	=		8

Look at what is needed on the left side to balance and what is on the right side. Do you see any patterns?

How can you use the numbers on the left side to figure out the number of clips or where to place the clips on the right side before you do it?

LEVELED LOADS

Apply the patterns you learned on the first page to predict the missing number in each row that will make the balance level.

Check your prediction by putting the clips at the correct positions to see if they balance.

QUANTITY OF CLIPS	VALUE OF POSITION	AND	QUANTITY OF CLIPS	VALUE OF POSITION	BALANCES	QUANTITY OF CLIPS	VALUE OF POSITION
2	6	+	2	8	=	4	
6	3	+	2	5	=		7
5	4	+	2		=	4	8
3	6	+		4	=	5	6
2		+	3	4	=	7	4
	6	+	3	4	=	3	8
2	7	+	2	5	=		8
3	8	+		4	=	4	8
3		+	1	3	=	3	8
3	7	+	3		=	6	6

Write an equation that generalizes your balanced solutions. (Use Q_1 for the first quantity, V_1 for the first value, Q_2 for the second quantity, V_2 for the second value, and Q_t for the total quantity, and V_t for the total value.)

LEVELED LOADS

The generalized equation for balance combinations is written below.

$$Q_1(V_1) + Q_2(V_2) = Q_T(V_T)$$

(Q_1 represents the first quantity, V_1 represents the first value, Q_2 represents the second quantity, V_2 represents the second value, Q_T represents the total quantity, and V_T represents the total value.)

Use the equation and your experiences with the balance to solve these problems.

1. If eight clips are placed three units from the center and two clips are placed eight units from the center on the left side of balance, where should four clips be placed on the right side to make the balance level?

2. A balance has five clips eight units from the center on the left side and three clips four units from the center on the right side. How many clips must be placed seven units from the center on the right side to make it level?

3. Six clips are placed both at nine units and three units from the center on one side of a balance. How many clips should be placed eight units from the center on the opposite side of the balance to make it level?

4. How many clips should be placed seven units to the left of center to balance a lever that also has seven clips three units to the left of center and five clips seven units to the right of center?

LEVELED LOADS

5. If eight pounds of peanuts that sell for $3 a pound are mixed with two pounds of cashews selling for $8 dollars a pound, you get 10 pounds of mixed nuts. What is the value of a pound of mixed nuts?

6. A mixture of eight pounds of nuts sells for $4 a pound. The mixture was made of six pounds of peanuts ($3 per pound) and two pounds of pecans. How much do pecans cost per pound?

7. Two pounds of peanuts ($3 per pound) are mixed with four pounds of raisins. The mixture sells for $2 a pound. How much did the raisins cost per pound?

8. A punch recipe calls for three gallons of pineapple juice and one gallon of orange juice ($8 per gallon). The punch sells for $11 per gallon. To break even on the four gallons of punch, how much should each gallon of pineapple juice cost?

9. Four gallons of grape juice ($6 per gallon) mixed with two gallons of apple juice ($6 per gallon) makes six gallons of fruit drink. How much does a gallon of fruit drink cost?

10. Fruit punch is made from two gallons of orange juice ($8 per gallon) and three gallons of cranberry juice ($10 per gallon). What is the cost per gallon of punch?

© 2007 AIMS Education Foundation

LEVELED LOADS

Connecting Learning

1. What patterns do you notice in the amount or placement of clips on a level balance?

2. How can you write your pattern as an equation?

3. How are the balance combination problems similar to other combination problems on the application page?

4. How can you use your generalized equation to solve similar problems about combinations?

146

SHADES OF GRAY

Topic
Solving equations: Mixture problems

Key Question
If you mix several shades of gray paint and you know the quantity of paint and the percent black of each shade, how can you determine the quantity and percent of black in the final mixture?

Learning Goals
Students will:
- draw representations of mixtures to determine numeric solutions,
- translate their drawn representations into numeric and algebraic equivalents to recognize numeric and algebraic methods of solution,
- apply their understanding from visual representations to translate word problems into algebraic form, and
- use algebraic methods to solve the problems.

Guiding Documents
Project 2061 Benchmarks
- *An equation containing a variable may be true for just one value of the variable.*
- *Mathematical statements can be used to describe how one quantity changes when another changes. Rates of change can be computed from magnitudes and vice versa.*
- *The operations + and – are inverses of each other— one undoes what the other does; likewise x and ÷.*

NCTM Standards 2000*
- *Develop an initial conceptual understanding of different uses of variables*
- *Use symbolic algebra to represent situations and to solve problems, especially those that involve linear relationships*
- *Recognize and generate equivalent forms for simple algebraic expressions and solve linear equations*

Math
Algebra
    solving equations
        mixtures

Integrated Processes
Observing
Comparing and contrasting
Generalizing

Materials
Student pages

Background Information
Mixing gray paint provides a simple context from which to develop a conceptual understanding of mixture problems. The quantity of paint comes in discrete units of cans. The value of the paint is the percent of the paint made up of black. The remaining paint is white, giving a variety of shades of gray.

A visual representation provides a means for students to readily find a solution to a mixture problem. Each can of paint can be represented with a square. The percent of black is represented by shading in the appropriate fraction of squares.

Consider the problem of mixing two cans of 50% paint with eight cans of 75% paint. The first set would be drawn with two squares with one shaded. The second set is represented by eight squares and six squares shaded. When the two sets are mixed or combined, there would be 10 squares with seven squares shaded. This could all be represented by the equation, $2(0.5) + 8(0.75) = 10(0.7)$

The drawn representation will help students recognize why the value of the mixture is closer to the value of one of the mixed parts than the other. In the example, there are four times more cans of 75% percent paint, causing the mixture to be much closer to the 75% paint than the 50% paint. This visual recognition provides a conceptual understanding of why a weighted or mixed average is not in the center of two values.

After doing a number of problems of this type, students will begin to recognize some patterns that will help them solve these problems more abstractly. First, the sum of the two quantities to be mixed is the total quantity of the mixture. Conversely, if you know the total quantity of the mixture, you can subtract the quantity of one of the parts to find the quantity of the other part. Second, the sum of the products of the quantity and value of the two parts to be mixed is equal to the product of the quantity and value of the mixture.

Management
1. This activity assumes students are familiar with percents and can convert fractions to percents and decimals.
2. Students should complete the activity *Leveled Loads* before doing this investigation.

Procedure

1. Distribute the first two student pages and explain the context of mixing paint. Have students consider the first problem and explain how the first two drawings represent two cans of 50% black paint and eight cans of 75% black paint.
2. Have the students color in the result of mixing the 10 cans of paint and record the solution as a percent in the written sentence.
3. Direct students to translate the written or pictured representation into an algebraic equation and then have them show the steps required to find the unknown percent.
4. Have students complete the problems on the first two pages by drawing a representation, finding the unknowns, and then summarizing the process with an equation and its solution.
5. When students have completed the first two pages, have them discuss the strategies they used to find the solutions.
6. Have students draw pictures or refer back to their experiences to solve the mixture problems on the last student page. These problems will help them generalize solution methods for typical abstract mixture problems found in an algebra book.

Connecting Learning

1. How do you determine how many squares to shade in the two mixed parts? [Convert the percent to a fraction and shade in the correct ratio of squares.]
2. How do you determine how many squares to make for the final mixture? [the sum of the quantity of cans of the two mixed parts]
3. How do you determine how many squares to shade in the final mixture? [the sum of the shaded squares in the two parts]
4. If you know how many cans of mixed paint you want, and you know how many cans of one type of paint you have, how do you determine how many cans of the other type of paint you will need? [Subtract the number of cans of the known type from the total to get the number of cans of the unknown type.]
5. How are your equations for all of the problems similar? [The sum of the products of the quantity and value of the parts is equal to the product of the mixed quantity and value.]
6. What is a general equation for mixing paint? [cans(percent) + cans(percent) = cans(percent), $Q_1(V_1) + Q_2(V_2) = Q_T(V_T)$]

Extension

Have students complete mixture problems from their textbooks and have them discuss how the problems are similar to and different from those they did in this investigation and how their solutions processes had to be adapted to these new problems.

Solutions

Page One
1. $2(0.5) + 8(0.75) = 10(\underline{0.7})$
2. $8(0.25) + 12(0.75) = 20(\underline{0.55})$
3. $8(0.75) + 12(0.25) = 20(\underline{0.45})$
4. $5(0.8) + 15(0.2) = 20(\underline{0.35})$

Page Two
5. $\underline{10}(\underline{0.2}) + 15(0.8) = 25(0.56)$
6. $4(0.75) + \underline{16}(\underline{0.25}) = 20(0.35)$
7. $\underline{5}(\underline{0.4}) + 20(0.8) = 25(0.72)$
8. $12(0.33) + 8(\underline{0.75}) = 20(0.5)$
9. $24(\underline{0.25}) + \underline{16}(0.75) = 40(0.45)$

Page Three
1a. $(x + 4)$
1b. $0.25(4) + 0.5x = 0.4(x + 4)$
1c. $x = 6$
2a. $(x + 3)$
2b. $0.6(3) + 0.15x = 0.3(x + 3)$
2c. $x = 6$
3a. $(x - 8)$
3b. $0.25(8) + 1(x - 8) = 0.5\,x$
3c. $x = 12$
4a. $(x - 15)$
4b. $0.8(15) + 0.3(x - 15) = 0.6\,x$
4c. $x = 25$

* Reprinted with permission from *Principles and Standards for School Mathematics*, 2000 by the National Council of Teachers of Mathematics. All rights reserved.

SHADES OF GRAY

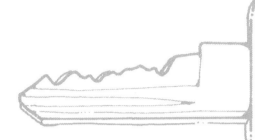

Key Question

If you mix several shades of gray paint and you know the quantity of paint and the percent black of each shade, how can you determine the quantity and percent of black in the final mixture?

Learning Goals

Students will:

- draw representations of mixtures to determine numeric solutions,

- translate their drawn representations into numeric and algebraic equivalents to recognize numeric and algebraic methods of solution,

- apply their understanding from visual representations to translate word problems into algebraic form, and

- use algebraic methods to solve the problems.

149

SHADES OF GRAY

Gray paint is a mixture of black and white. The darkness of the gray is described in percent black. Determine the percent black or number of cans needed to make each of the following combinations. When you have shaded the pictures, make a number sentence to describe the mixing and outcome.

1. Two cans of 50% mixed with eight cans of 75% makes 10 cans of _____%

   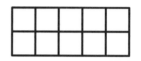

2. Eight cans of 25% mixed with 12 cans of 75% makes 20 cans of _____%

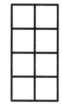 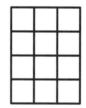 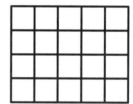

3. Eight cans of 75% mixed with 12 cans of 25% makes _____ cans of _____%

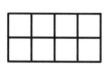 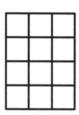

4. Five cans of 80% mixed with 15 cans of 20% makes _____ cans of _____%

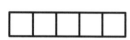 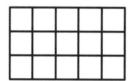

150

SHADES OF GRAY

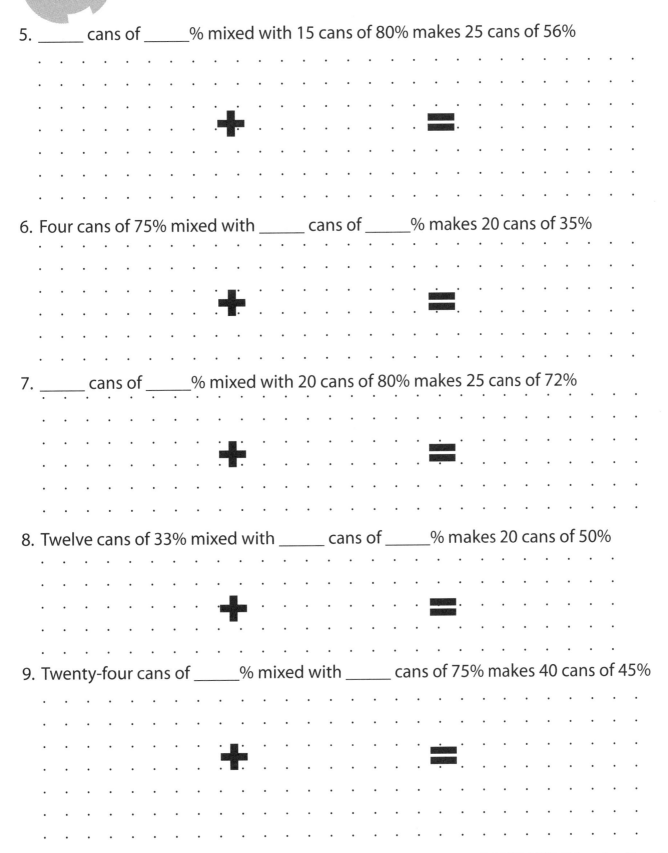

5. _____ cans of _____% mixed with 15 cans of 80% makes 25 cans of 56%

6. Four cans of 75% mixed with _____ cans of _____% makes 20 cans of 35%

7. _____ cans of _____% mixed with 20 cans of 80% makes 25 cans of 72%

8. Twelve cans of 33% mixed with _____ cans of _____% makes 20 cans of 50%

9. Twenty-four cans of _____% mixed with _____ cans of 75% makes 40 cans of 45%

151

SHADES OF GRAY

1. You have four cans of 25% black paint. How many cans of 50% black paint do you need to mix to get 40% black paint?

   a. If x represents the number of 50% black paint cans, how many cans of mixed paint will there be?

   b. Write an equation showing that the two types of paints, when mixed, are equal to the final mixture.

   c. Solve the equation by distributing and isolating x.

2. You have three cans of 60% black paint. How many cans of 15% black paint do you need to mix to get 30% black paint?

   a. If x represents the number of 15% black paint cans, how many cans of mixed paint will there be?

   b. Write an equation showing that the two types of paints, when mixed, are equal to the final mixture.

   c. Solve the equation by distributing and isolating x.

3. If eight cans of 25% black paint are mixed with 100% black paint until it is 50% black paint, how many cans of mixed paint will there be?

   a. If x represents the number cans of mixed 50% black paint, how many cans of 100% black paint were added to the mixture?

   b. Write an equation showing that the two types of paints, when mixed, are equal to the final mixture.

   c. Solve the equation by distributing and isolating x.

4. If 15 cans of 80% black paint are mixed with 30% black paint until it is 60% black paint, how many cans of mixed paint will there be?

   a. If x represents the number cans of mixed 60% black paint, how many cans of 30% black paint were added to the mixture?

   b. Write an equation showing that the two types of paints, when mixed, are equal to the final mixture.

   c. Solve the equation by distributing and isolating x.

152

SHADES OF GRAY

Connecting Learning

1. How do you determine how many squares to shade in the two mixed parts?

2. How do you determine how many squares to make for the final mixture?

3. How do you determine how many squares to shade in the final mixture?

4. If you know how many cans of mixed paint you want, and you know how many cans of one type of paint you have, how do you determine how many cans of the other type of paint you will need?

5. How are your equations for all of the problems similar?

6. What is a general equation for mixing paint?

153

WATERED DOWN TEMPERATURES

Topic
Solving equations: Mixture problems

Key Question
If you mix two samples of water at different temperatures, how can you predict the temperature of the water after the samples mix?

Learning Goals
Students will:
- use a simulator to mix samples of water at different temperatures and record the outcomes,
- recognize patterns in their records that will allow them to generalize procedures of predicting mixed water temperatures, and
- apply their generalized procedures to predict mixed water temperatures and verify the predictions with the simulator.

Guiding Documents
Project 2061 Benchmarks
- *An equation containing a variable may be true for just one value of the variable.*
- *Mathematical statements can be used to describe how one quantity changes when another changes. Rates of change can be computed from magnitudes and vice versa.*
- *The operations + and – are inverses of each other— one undoes what the other does; likewise x and ÷.*

NCTM Standards 2000*
- *Develop an initial conceptual understanding of different uses of variables*
- *Use symbolic algebra to represent situations and to solve problems, especially those that involve linear relationships*
- *Recognize and generate equivalent forms for simple algebraic expressions and solve linear equations*

Math
Algebra
   solving equations
      mixtures

Integrated Processes
Observing
Comparing and contrasting
Generalizing

Materials
Computers (see *Management 3*)
Water Temperature Calculator (see *Management 2*)
Student pages

Background Information
Students have had the experience of mixing different temperatures of water from playing at a sink or running a bath. This experience provides an intuitive background for the simulation in this activity. Students recognize that a large bowl of very hot steaming soup is cooled only slightly by a spoonful of very cold milk. However, if a large glass of milk is poured into the bowl, the soup becomes lukewarm. From experience, students understand that the mixed temperature of two liquids is affected by both the temperatures and quantities of the liquids.

A simulator provides the opportunity to quickly experiment with mixing different quantities and temperatures of liquids. As students investigate in an organized way, they come to recognize that when equal quantities of different temperature liquids are mixed, the resulting temperature is a simple average of the two temperatures. They also notice that the quantity of mixed liquid is the sum of quantities of the two combined parts. As students work with mixtures made of differing quantities, they will notice that, although the final mixed quantity remains the sum of the parts, the temperature is affected by the proportions of the two mixed quantities to the total mixture.

When students are asked to focus on how can they operate on the numbers of quantity and temperature in the two mixed parts to get the numbers in the total mixture, they begin to recognize that the sum of the products of each mixed quantity and temperature equals the product of the final quantity and temperature. If students have done some work with mixtures prior to this investigation, they will more quickly see the patterns in the results. Students who are moving to more abstract understanding can be encouraged to develop and record the pattern in a generalized mixture equation, $Q_1(V_1) + Q_2(V_2) = Q_T(V_T)$ where Q represents quantity and V represents the temperature value.

Management
1. *Leveled Loads* provides a more concrete experience and should be done prior to this investigation.
2. Prepare computers for student use by loading the *Water Temperature Calculator* on each. The calculator can be found on the accompanying DVD or online at: URL: www.aimsedu.org/media/books.
3. The best situation is to have two students per computer, though small groups of four work nearly as well. If only a single computer is available in the classroom, the monitor can be turned toward the students and a volunteer can enter the class's suggestions.

154

Procedure

1. Have a discussion with students about their experiences with mixing liquids. Have them discuss situations such as what they think would happen to the temperature of a large bowl of steaming soup if you mixed in a spoonful of cold milk or a large glass of cold milk. Then pose the *Key Question* to elicit expectations for more exacting predictions with number.
2. Distribute the first student page and provide the students access to a computer with the flash simulator *Water Temperature Calculator*.
3. Have students discuss and predict the outcome for each of the trials. Then have them enter the input data into the simulator and compare the outcome to their prediction. Have them record the outcome data.
4. Discuss with the students what patterns they see in the data and how they can accurately predict the final temperature using the input data and their patterns. If it is appropriate, have them generalize the patterns and/or procedures with an equation.
5. Distribute the second student page and have students use their patterns, procedures, or generalized equations to find the missing data. Allow the students to use the simulator to verify their predictions.
6. Distribute the third student page to help students learn how to work backwards and determine the correct quantity to add to get the final mixture to be the correct temperature. Allow students to use the simulator to confirm their work.

Connecting Learning

1. How do you determine volume of the final mixture? [find the sum of the quantity of the two mixed parts]
2. When is the final temperature right in the middle of the two temperatures used in the mixture? [when the same amounts are mixed]
3. How can you tell if the final temperature will be closer to the colder or hotter temperature of the two mixed parts? [The temperature will be closer to the temperature that is greatest in quantity. The greater the difference in quantity, the closer the final temperature will be to the temperature of the greater quantity.]
4. How can you use the numbers of the two parts mixed to get the numbers of the final mixture? [The sum of the products of the quantity and temperature of the parts is equal to the product of the mixed quantity and temperature.]
5. What is a general equation for mixing two temperatures of water? [$Q_1(V_1) + Q_2(V_2) = Q_T(V_T)$, where Q represents quantity and V represents the temperature value.]

Extensions

1. Have students compare problems in their textbooks to the problems in this investigation and have them determine how to use the simulator to find solutions to the textbook problems. Have the students discuss modifications they had to make in their thinking to utilize the simulator.
2. Have students complete mixture problems from their textbooks and have them discuss how the problems are similar to and different from those they did in this investigation and how their solution processes had to be adapted to these new problems.

Solutions

Page One

Trial 1: $2(5) + 2(15) = 4(10)$
Trial 2: $3(10) + 3(30) = 6(20)$
Trial 3: $1(10) + 3(30) = 4(25)$
Trial 4: $3(10) + 1(30) = 4(15)$
Trial 5: $2(10) + 3(20) = 5(16)$
Trial 6: $3(10) + 2(20) = 5(14)$
Trial 7: $1(10) + 4(30) = 5(26)$
Trial 8: $4(10) + 1(30) = 5(14)$
Trial 9: $2(10) + 4(40) = 6(30)$
Trial 10: $4(10) + 2(40) = 6(20)$

Page Two

Trial 1: $3(25) + 2(75) = 5(45)$
Trial 2: $5(10) + 3(26) = 8(16)$
Trial 3: $4(10) + 3(24) = 7(16)$
Trial 4: $5(10) + 3(50) = 8(25)$
Trial 5: $6(5) + 3(95) = 9(35)$
Trial 6: $2(10) + 5(80) = 7(60)$
Trial 7: $3(10) + 4(80) = 7(50)$
Trial 8: $4(25) + 6(50) = 10(40)$
Trial 9: $8.33(10) + 5(50) = 13.33(25)$
Trial 10: $0.5(10) + 1(100) = 1.5(70)$
Trial 11: $x = 8.33(8) + 5(48) = 13.33(23)$
Trial 12: $x = 0.8(10) + 1(100) = 1.8(60)$

Page Three

1. a. $x + 0.25$
   b. $0.25(42) + x(60) = (x + 0.25)(54)$
   c. $x = 0.5$
2. a. $x + 0.4$
   b. $x(10) + 0.4(25) = (x + 0.4)(16)$
   c. $x = 0.6$
3. a. $x - 1.5$
   b. $(x - 1.5)(10) + 1.5(30) = x(18)$
   c. $x = 3.75$
4. a. $x - 0.75$
   b. $0.75(25) + (x - 0.75)(100) = x(55)$
   c. $x = 1.25$

* Reprinted with permission from *Principles and Standards for School Mathematics*, 2000 by the National Council of Teachers of Mathematics. All rights reserved.

WATERED DOWN TEMPERATURES

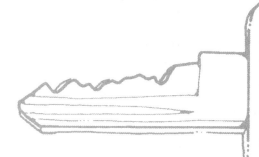

Key Question

If you mix two samples of water at different temperatures, how can you predict the temperature of the water after the samples mix?

Learning Goals

Students will:

- use a simulator to mix samples of water at different temperatures and record the outcomes,
- recognize patterns in their records that will allow them to generalize procedures of predicting mixed water temperatures, and

- apply their generalized procedures to predict mixed water temperatures and verify the predictions with the simulator.

WATERED DOWN TEMPERATURES

Use the *Mixing Temperature Calculator* to mix the two samples of water and record the volume and temperature of each trial's mixture.

	SAMPLE ONE (VOLUME · TEMPERATURE)		+	SAMPLE TWO (VOLUME · TEMPERATURE)		=	MIXTURE (VOLUME · TEMPERATURE)	
TRIAL 1:	2	5	+	2	15	=		
TRIAL 2:	3	10	+	3	30	=		
TRIAL 3:	1	10	+	3	30	=		
TRIAL 4:	3	10	+	1	30	=		
TRIAL 5:	2	10	+	3	20	=		
TRIAL 6:	3	10	+	2	20	=		
TRIAL 7:	1	10	+	4	30	=		
TRIAL 8:	4	10	+	1	30	=		
TRIAL 9:	2	10	+	4	40	=		
TRIAL 10:	4	10	+	2	40	=		

1. How can you determine the volume of the mixture without the calculator?

2. Except for the first two trials, why is the mixed temperature not in the middle of the two sample temperatures?

3. How can you determine the temperature of the mixture without the calculator?

WATERED DOWN TEMPERATURES

Determine what volumes or temperatures are needed to get the missing temperature. Then check your accuracy with the *Mixing Temperature Calculator*.

	SAMPLE ONE (VOLUME · TEMPERATURE)		+	SAMPLE TWO (VOLUME · TEMPERATURE)		=	MIXTURE (VOLUME · TEMPERATURE)	
TRIAL 1:	3	· 25	+	2	· 75	=		·
TRIAL 2:	5	· 10	+	3	· 26	=		·
TRIAL 3:	4	· 10	+		·	=	7	· 16
TRIAL 4:		·	+	3	· 50	=	8	· 25
TRIAL 5:	6	· 5	+		·	=	9	· 35
TRIAL 6:		·	+	5	· 80	=	7	· 60
TRIAL 7:	3	· 10	+		· 80	=		· 50
TRIAL 8:	4	· 25	+		· 50	=		· 40
TRIAL 9:		· 10	+	5	· 50	=		· 25
TRIAL 10:		· 10	+	1	· 100	=		· 70

TRIAL 11: You want the perfect bath water—23° Celsius (body temperature). You have five gallons of water heated to 48° Celsius. How many gallons of 8° tap water do you need to add to your heated water for the perfect bath?

TRIAL 12: A bread recipe calls for 60° Celsius water. You have heated one cup of water to boiling—100°. How much 10° tap water do you need to add to get the correct temperature water for your recipe?

WATERED DOWN TEMPERATURES

1. You have 0.25 gallons of 42° water. How many gallons of 60° water do you need to mix to get 54° water?

   a. If *x* represents the gallons of 60° water, how many gallons of mixed water will there be?

   b. Write an equation showing that the two temperatures of water are mixed to get 54° water.

   c. Solve the equation by distributing and isolating *x*.

2. You have 0.4 gallons of 25° water. How many gallons of 10° water do you need to mix to get 16° water?

   a. If *x* represents the gallons of 10° water, how many gallons of mixed water will there be?

   b. Write an equation showing that the two temperatures of water are mixed to get 16° water.

   c. Solve the equation by distributing and isolating *x*.

3. If 1.5 gallons of 30° water are mixed with 10° water until it is 18°, how many gallons of 18° water will there be?

   a. If *x* represents the gallons of 18° water, how many gallons of 10° water were added to the mixture?

   b. Write an equation showing that the two temperatures of water, when mixed, are equal to the final mixture.

   c. Solve the equation by distributing and isolating *x*.

4. If .75 gallons of 25° water are mixed with 100° water until is 55°, how many gallons of 55° water will there be?

   a. If *x* represents the gallons of 55° water, how many gallons of 100° water were added to the mixture?

   b. Write an equation showing that the two temperatures of water, when mixed, are equal to the final mixture.

   c. Solve the equation by distributing and isolating *x*.

WATERED DOWN TEMPERATURES

Connecting Learning

1. How do you determine volume of the final mixture?

2. When is the final temperature right in the middle of the two temperatures used in the mixture?

3. How can you tell if the final temperature will be closer to the colder or hotter temperature of the two mixed parts?

4. How can you use the numbers of the two parts mixed to get the numbers of the final mixture?

5. What is a general equation for mixing two temperatures of water?

The AIMS Program

AIMS is the acronym for "**A**ctivities **I**ntegrating **M**athematics and **S**cience." Such integration enriches learning and makes it meaningful and holistic. AIMS began as a project of Fresno Pacific University to integrate the study of mathematics and science in grades K-9, but has since expanded to include language arts, social studies, and other disciplines.

AIMS is a continuing program of the non-profit AIMS Education Foundation. It had its inception in a National Science Foundation funded program whose purpose was to explore the effectiveness of integrating mathematics and science. The project directors, in cooperation with 80 elementary classroom teachers, devoted two years to a thorough field-testing of the results and implications of integration.

The approach met with such positive results that the decision was made to launch a program to create instructional materials incorporating this concept. Despite the fact that thoughtful educators have long recommended an integrative approach, very little appropriate material was available in 1981 when the project began. A series of writing projects ensued, and today the AIMS Education Foundation is committed to continuing the creation of new integrated activities on a permanent basis.

The AIMS program is funded through the sale of books, products, and professional-development workshops, and through proceeds from the Foundation's endowment. All net income from programs and products flows into a trust fund administered by the AIMS Education Foundation. Use of these funds is restricted to support of research, development, and publication of new materials. Writers donate all their rights to the Foundation to support its ongoing program. No royalties are paid to the writers.

The rationale for integration lies in the fact that science, mathematics, language arts, social studies, etc., are integrally interwoven in the real world, from which it follows that they should be similarly treated in the classroom where students are being prepared to live in that world. Teachers who use the AIMS program give enthusiastic endorsement to the effectiveness of this approach.

Science encompasses the art of questioning, investigating, hypothesizing, discovering, and communicating. Mathematics is a language that provides clarity, objectivity, and understanding. The language arts provide us with powerful tools of communication. Many of the major contemporary societal issues stem from advancements in science and must be studied in the context of the social sciences. Therefore, it is timely that all of us take seriously a more holistic method of educating our students. This goal motivates all who are associated with the AIMS Program. We invite you to join us in this effort.

Meaningful integration of knowledge is a major recommendation coming from the nation's professional science and mathematics associations. The American Association for the Advancement of Science in *Science for All Americans* strongly recommends the integration of mathematics, science, and technology. The National Council of Teachers of Mathematics places strong emphasis on applications of mathematics found in science investigations. AIMS is fully aligned with these recommendations.

Extensive field testing of AIMS investigations confirms these beneficial results:

1. Mathematics becomes more meaningful, hence more useful, when it is applied to situations that interest students.
2. The extent to which science is studied and understood is increased when mathematics and science are integrated.
3. There is improved quality of learning and retention, supporting the thesis that learning which is meaningful and relevant is more effective.
4. Motivation and involvement are increased dramatically as students investigate real-world situations and participate actively in the process.

We invite you to become part of this classroom teacher movement by using an integrated approach to learning and sharing any suggestions you may have. The AIMS Program welcomes you!

AIMS Education Foundation Programs

Practical proven strategies to improve student achievement

When you host an AIMS workshop for elementary and middle school educators, you will know your teachers are receiving effective usable training they can apply in their classrooms immediately.

Designed for teachers—AIMS Workshops:
- Correlate to your state standards;
- Address key topic areas, including math content, science content, problem solving, and process skills;
- Teach you how to use AIMS' effective hands-on approach;
- Provide practice of activity-based teaching;
- Address classroom management issues, higher-order thinking skills, and materials;
- Give you AIMS resources; and
- Offer college (graduate-level) credits for many courses.

Aligned to district and administrator needs—AIMS workshops offer:
- Flexible scheduling and grade span options;
- Custom (one-, two-, or three-day) workshops to meet specific schedule, topic and grade-span needs;
- Pre-packaged one-day workshops on most major topics—only $3900 for up to 30 participants (includes all materials and expenses);
- Prepackaged four- or five-day workshops for in-depth math and science training—only $12,300 for up to 30 participants (includes all materials and expenses);
- Sustained staff development, by scheduling workshops throughout the school year and including follow-up and assessment;
- Eligibility for funding under the Title I and Title II sections of No Child Left Behind; and

- Affordable professional development—save when you schedule consecutive-day workshops.

University Credit—Correspondence Courses

AIMS offers correspondence courses through a partnership with Fresno Pacific University.
- Convenient distance-learning courses—you study at your own pace and schedule. No computer or Internet access required!

The tuition for each three-semester unit graduate-level course is $264 plus a materials fee.

The AIMS Instructional Leadership Program

This is an AIMS staff-development program seeking to prepare facilitators for leadership roles in science/math education in their home districts or regions. Upon successful completion of the program, trained facilitators become members of the AIMS Instructional Leadership Network, qualified to conduct AIMS workshops, teach AIMS in-service courses for college credit, and serve as AIMS consultants. Intensive training is provided in mathematics, science, process and thinking skills, workshop management, and other relevant topics.

Introducing AIMS Science Core Curriculum

Developed to meet 100% of your state's standards, AIMS' Science Core Curriculum gives students the opportunity to build content knowledge, thinking skills, and fundamental science processes.
- *Each* grade specific module has been developed to extend the AIMS approach to full-year science programs.
- *Each* standards-based module includes math, reading, hands-on investigations, and assessments.

Like all AIMS resources, these core modules are able to serve students at all stages of readiness, making these a great value across the grades served in your school.

For current information regarding the programs described above, please complete the following form and mail it to: P.O. Box 8120, Fresno, CA 93747.

Information Request

Please send current information on the items checked:

_____ *Basic Information Packet* on AIMS materials _____ Hosting information for AIMS workshops
_____ *AIMS Instructional Leadership Program* _____ AIMS Science Core Curriculum

Name _____ Phone _____

Address_____
        Street   City   State   Zip

Magazine

YOUR K-9 MATH AND SCIENCE
CLASSROOM ACTIVITIES RESOURCE

The AIMS Magazine is your source for standards-based, hands-on math and science investigations. Each issue is filled with teacher-friendly, ready-to-use activities that engage students in meaningful learning.

- *Four issues each year (fall, winter, spring, and summer).*

Current issue is shipped with all past issues within that volume.

| 1822 | Volume XXII | 2007-2008 | $19.95 |
| 1823 | Volume XXIII | 2008-2009 | $19.95 |

Two-Volume Combination

| M20709 | Volumes XXII & XXIII | 2007-2009 | $34.95 |
| M20810 | Volumes XXIII & XXIV | 2008-2010 | $34.95 |

Back Volumes Available
Complete volumes available for purchase:

1802	Volume II	1987-1988	$19.95
1804	Volume IV	1989-1990	$19.95
1805	Volume V	1990-1991	$19.95
1807	Volume VII	1992-1993	$19.95
1808	Volume VIII	1993-1994	$19.95
1809	Volume IX	1994-1995	$19.95
1810	Volume X	1995-1996	$19.95
1811	Volume XI	1996-1997	$19.95
1812	Volume XII	1997-1998	$19.95
1813	Volume XIII	1998-1999	$19.95
1814	Volume XIV	1999-2000	$19.95
1815	Volume XV	2000-2001	$19.95
1816	Volume XVI	2001-2002	$19.95
1817	Volume XVII	2002-2003	$19.95
1818	Volume XVIII	2003-2004	$19.95
1819	Volume XIX	2004-2005	$19.95
1820	Volume XX	2005-2006	$19.95
1821	Volume XXI	2006-2007	$19.95

Volumes II to XIX include 10 issues.

Call 1.888.733.2467 or go to www.aimsedu.org

Subscribe to the AIMS Magazine

$19.95 a year!

AIMS Magazine is published four times a year.

Subscriptions ordered at any time will receive all the issues for that year.

AIMS Online—www.aimsedu.org

To see all that AIMS has to offer, check us out on the Internet at www.aimsedu.org. At our website you can search our activities database; preview and purchase individual AIMS activities; learn about core curriculum, college courses, and workshops; buy manipulatives and other classroom resources; and download free resources including articles, puzzles, and sample AIMS activities.

AIMS News
While visiting the AIMS website, sign up for AIMS News, our FREE e-mail newsletter. You'll get the latest information on what's new at AIMS including:

- New publications;
- New core curriculum modules; and
- New materials.

Sign up today!

AIMS Program Publications

Actions with Fractions, 4-9
Awesome Addition and Super Subtraction, 2-3
Bats Incredible! 2-4
Brick Layers II, 4-9
Chemistry Matters, 4-7
Counting on Coins, K-2
Cycles of Knowing and Growing, 1-3
Crazy about Cotton, 3-7
Critters, 2-5
Earth Book, 6-9
Electrical Connections, 4-9
Exploring Environments, K-6
Fabulous Fractions, 3-6
Fall into Math and Science, K-1
Field Detectives, 3-6
Finding Your Bearings, 4-9
Floaters and Sinkers, 5-9
From Head to Toe, 5-9
Fun with Foods, 5-9
Glide into Winter with Math and Science, K-1
Gravity Rules! 5-12
Hardhatting in a Geo-World, 3-5
It's About Time, K-2
It Must Be A Bird, Pre-K-2
Jaw Breakers and Heart Thumpers, 3-5
Looking at Geometry, 6-9
Looking at Lines, 6-9
Machine Shop, 5-9
Magnificent Microworld Adventures, 5-9
Marvelous Multiplication and Dazzling Division, 4-5
Math + Science, A Solution, 5-9
Mostly Magnets, 2-8
Movie Math Mania, 6-9
Multiplication the Algebra Way, 6-8
Off the Wall Science, 3-9
Out of This World, 4-8
Paper Square Geometry:
    The Mathematics of Origami, 5-12
Puzzle Play, 4-8
Pieces and Patterns, 5-9
Popping With Power, 3-5
Positive vs. Negative, 6-9
Primarily Bears, K-6
Primarily Earth, K-3
Primarily Physics, K-3

Primarily Plants, K-3
Problem Solving: Just for the Fun of It! 4-9
Problem Solving: Just for the Fun of It! Book Two, 4-9
Proportional Reasoning, 6-9
Ray's Reflections, 4-8
Sensational Springtime, K-2
Sense-Able Science, K-1
Soap Films and Bubbles, 4-9
Solve It! K-1: Problem-Solving Strategies, K-1
Solve It! 2nd: Problem-Solving Strategies, 2
Solve It! 3rd: Problem-Solving Strategies, 3
Solve It! 4th: Problem-Solving Strategies, 4
Solve It! 5th: Problem-Solving Strategies, 5
Solving Equations: A Conceptual Approach, 6-9
Spatial Visualization, 4-9
Spills and Ripples, 5-12
Spring into Math and Science, K-1
The Amazing Circle, 4-9
The Budding Botanist, 3-6
The Sky's the Limit, 5-9
Through the Eyes of the Explorers, 5-9
Under Construction, K-2
Water Precious Water, 2-6
Weather Sense: Temperature, Air Pressure, and Wind, 4-5
Weather Sense: Moisture, 4-5
Winter Wonders, K-2

Spanish Supplements*
Fall Into Math and Science, K-1
Glide Into Winter with Math and Science, K-1
Mostly Magnets, 2-8
Pieces and Patterns, 5-9
Primarily Bears, K-6
Primarily Physics, K-3
Sense-Able Science, K-1
Spring Into Math and Science, K-1

* Spanish supplements are only available as downloads from the AIMS website. The supplements contain only the student pages in Spanish; you will need the English version of the book for the teacher's text.

Spanish Edition
Constructores II: Ingeniería Creativa Con Construcciones
    LEGO® 4-9
    The entire book is written in Spanish. English pages not included.

Other Publications
Historical Connections in Mathematics, Vol. I, 5-9
Historical Connections in Mathematics, Vol. II, 5-9
Historical Connections in Mathematics, Vol. III, 5-9
Mathematicians are People, Too
Mathematicians are People, Too, Vol. II
What's Next, Volume 1, 4-12
What's Next, Volume 2, 4-12
What's Next, Volume 3, 4-12

For further information, contact:
AIMS Education Foundation • P.O. Box 8120 • Fresno, California 93747-8120
www.aimsedu.org • 559.255.6396 (fax) • 888.733.2467 (toll free)

Duplication Rights

Standard Duplication Rights

Purchasers of AIMS activities (individually or in books and magazines) may make up to 200 copies of any portion of the purchased activities, provided these copies will be used for educational purposes and only at one school site.

Workshop or conference presenters may make one copy of a purchased activity for each participant, with a limit of five activities per workshop or conference session.

Standard duplication rights apply to activities received at workshops, free sample activities provided by AIMS, and activities received by conference participants.

All copies must bear the AIMS Education Foundation copyright information.

Unlimited Duplication Rights

To ensure compliance with copyright regulations, AIMS users may upgrade from standard to unlimited duplication rights. Such rights permit unlimited duplication of purchased activities (including revisions) for use at a given school site.

Activities received at workshops are eligible for upgrade from standard to unlimited duplication rights.

Free sample activities and activities received as a conference participant are not eligible for upgrade from standard to unlimited duplication rights.

Upgrade Fees

The fees for upgrading from standard to unlimited duplication rights are:
- $5 per activity per site,
- $25 per book per site, and
- $10 per magazine issue per site.

The cost of upgrading is shown in the following examples:
- activity: 5 activities x 5 sites x $5 = $125
- book: 10 books x 5 sites x $25 = $1250
- magazine issue: 1 issue x 5 sites x $10 = $50

Purchasing Unlimited Duplication Rights

To purchase unlimited duplication rights, please provide us the following:
1. The name of the individual responsible for coordinating the purchase of duplication rights.
2. The title of each book, activity, and magazine issue to be covered.
3. The number of school sites and name of each site for which rights are being purchased.
4. Payment (check, purchase order, credit card)

Requested duplication rights are automatically authorized with payment. The individual responsible for coordinating the purchase of duplication rights will be sent a certificate verifying the purchase.

Internet Use

Permission to make AIMS activities available on the Internet is determined on a case-by-case basis.

- P. O. Box 8120, Fresno, CA 93747-8120 -
- aimsed@aimsedu.org - www.aimsedu.org -
- 559.255.6396 (fax) - 888.733.2467 (toll free) -